A Special Gift

Presented To

_____

From

_____

Date

_____

Message

_____

_____

_____

D1496094

i

13 Moons
A balanced feminine approach to living in flow of daily devotion and cyclical planning

Jennifer L. Mons

All rights reserved Jennifer L Mons LLC © 2022

ISBN 979-8-9860445-0-7
Editor/Print Genius Books & Media, Inc.
www.jenmons.com

Facebook Jen Mons Coaching
Facebook Groups
https://www.facebook.com/groups/13moonsdevotion
https://www.facebook.com/groups/5elementwellth

Instagram @jen.mons
Twitter @jennymons

Share images of your journaling experience
#13moonsdailydevotion #5elementwellth

Other offerings with Jen Mons (see resources for links)

Retreats
Daily Devotion and 13 Moons Membership
Prosperity
North Star Collective & 5 Element Well-th
Coach Training & Mentorship
Body and Soul Wisdom Podcast

This content is being provided to you for your individual use. You are not permitted
or authorized to copy, share, sell, post, distribute, reproduce, duplicate, trade,
resell, exploit, or otherwise disseminate any portion of this content for business or
commercial use, or in any other way that earns you money, without my prior written
permission. This journal is for educational and personal development purposes
only and not meant to replace support from any kind of healthcare professional
or services. Please seek appropriate professional advice regarding physical or
physiological conditions or concerns.
Jennifer L Mons LLC and Jen Mons Coaching ©

Table of Contents

Aloha and Welcome!

I am so honored that you have chosen to connect, share, expand, and grow through this journaling experience. As a lifelong student, teacher, and facilitator of transformation and growth, journaling has played a key role throughout my journey and coaching career. This journal will help bring clarity, intention, and ease into your life. I believe "Life is 10% what happens to you and 90% how you react" as Charles R Swindall said.

In my own words, you, I, **we get to be the authors of our own life story**. This journal is the beginning to becoming the author of your story.

You cannot change the past and where you have been, but you get to choose **who you are becoming**.

This journal provides space for awareness, clarity, and intention to guide you to align your life to live the way you truly want to live.

Where it began...

Daily Devotion and Journaling
When I graduated high school in 1995, my swim coach John gave me a beautiful bound journal as a gift with a letter inside. I was embarking on a courageous and adventurous choice to attend the Merchant Marine

Academy in Long Island, NY, leaving behind a comfortable version of me and stepping into a life of adventure, uncertainty, and growth while sailing around the world on ships as part of my studies in school. He encouraged me to keep a journal, and so my on and off relationship with journaling began in 1995. I journaled through my 350 days at sea, through falling in love with my soulmate husband, our engagement, 9/11, my marriage, wanting to become a mother, my near death birthing experience, and into growing my evolving coaching practice since 2009. There were months, even years while my kids were young that maybe I only wrote once a year, but I always found my way back to journaling through both the challenging and joyful times in life.

Cyclical Living

When I began coaching part time as a young mother in 2009, I still fell into my old patterns of overworking and perfecting, trying to find the time to balance work and family. In 2018, I decided to shift and take up more space as a business owner and coach/mentor. That meant I could no longer work the way I used to. After overcoming two stress-related health crises in 2006 and 2014, it became clear that I was in a pattern of "proving myself" and on my way to burnout. I began healing my relationship to feminine energy, something that had not been part of my life as a former engineer and military reservist. I let go of the hustle and stepped into alignment through cyclical planning around my menstrual cycle, the four seasons, and the monthly moon cycles.

If you are navigating overwhelm, busyness, procrastination, indecision, perfectionism, hustle, people pleasing, and low energy, then you are ready to choose daily alignment and welcome more fulfillment, success, and freedom into all parts of your life. This journal is designed to help you deepen your awareness to what you are meant to align your life to.

I hope that you will allow this experience to crack your heart open, reveal your innermost desires, facilitate gentle healing, and explore the hidden gems within you. May you continue to grow and flourish through the devotion to this journaling experience as if they are written conversations with God—or whatever higher power you believe in. May you discover the gentle healing of relationships by revealing clarity, needs, and feelings you are navigating in all parts of life.

With Love, Gratitude, and Aloha!

Jenny Mons

Our Why and Mission

Imagine what your life will be like a year from now if you fully commit to this experience. You now create a small intention each day (big win already). You align your intention and actions to your goals through awareness and growth each month. Lastly, you give yourself permission to welcome more energy, clarity, and ease now that you are aligned with the cyclical flow of life.

This is not a planner, it is not a self-help book; this is a journey of self-discovery through awareness of and curiosity about the wholeness of you.

Give yourself permission to navigate this experience. There is no right or wrong, only clarity on what is working and what is not.

This is an opportunity to reveal the hidden gems within you. A sacred space for growth, self-awareness, and clarity about how to align your life with your soul path. This journal experience will help you build the foundation for a fulfilling life through alignment with healthy relationships and redefining boundaries. It will help you **embody** the person **you are becoming** versus "doing the things" you think you *have* to do.

If you are living on autopilot, too busy to make time for what matters most, you are experiencing a misalignment, and you are likely feeling tired and unfulfilled. This journal will help you welcome your soul alignment to your truth and life story.

Everything begins with INTENTION. Where intention goes, ENERGY FLOWS. *You were my intention when I created this.*

From there you reach DEVOTION, a heart- and soul-centered dedication or commitment to yourself, your time, and your daily journaling and gratitude practice.

The next step is to expand that daily practice into monthly reflections and celebrations through a cyclical NEW MOON Planning/Ceremony.

Then you will be able to check in each season to realign and redirect your energy based on what you are learning, your growth, your goals— and your natural energy flow.

At the end of a calendar year, 365 days, 13 moons, and 4 seasons, you will have a space to reflect and reframe for the upcoming year.

This journal will serve as a recording of your growth, goals, and reflections throughout the next 365 days to give you clarity on how to navigate the flow of your life.

Create your natural rhythm

Like everything in life, there is no one size fits all. I began a cyclical approach to work/life balance in 2018 as my professional life began to expand. Using this approach, I watched everything in my life flourish. This journal serves as a template and guide to empower, equip, and guide you in creating more flow in your life. You are invited to embody this experience in a way that aligns with your natural flow—and you will be given the tools to do so.

This is not intended to be another item to check off your to-do list; rather it is your decision to shift your energy to living with intention each day, month, and seasonal cycle.

Why The New Moon

Everything has a phase or cycle. The moon has 4 phases. The New Moon represents the energy of a new beginning, planting seeds, setting intentions, and offering creative expression.

Learning to manage your energy with the natural flow of Mother Nature's energy can radically improve your well-being. If we are made up of between 45%-75% water depending on our age and other factors, and the moon affects the tide and the 70% ocean that makes up our planet, then it's safe to acknowledge that we may be affected by the moon as well. When you look around outside, all plants and animals, except for human beings, adapt to daily, monthly, and seasonal changes. This is an invitation to explore intention setting through the feminine and cyclical approach with each new moon.

My Mission is for you to be able to create a balanced feminine approach to living in the flow of daily devotion and cyclical planning.

This is a space for you to reflect and grow daily, set intentions monthly, and align your energy with the 4 seasons, to learn and implement energy management over time management so that you can have more time, freedom, and energy for the life you love.

Enjoy the Journey!

Who This Journal is For

This journal is for you if you feel busy, overwhelmed, and tired from the daily demands of life, and you are at a point in your life where you want clarity on what is working and what is not. In today's world, busyness has become the best distraction from what actually fulfills us in life.

What if being busy and feeling overwhelmed are just here to show you where you are misaligned? What if you lean into energy alignment through intention, flow, and ease?

Where intention flows, energy goes

➢ You want clarity, flow, and ease in your life topped with the confidence to choose wisely

➢ You are tired of the busyness, misalignment, and overwhelm

➢ You are ready to live your life with intention so that you can look back and celebrate your life

➢ You are willing to explore energy management over time management

➤ You are willing to integrate a blended balance of flow and structure into your life

➤ You are ready to give yourself permission to start each day with intention and to align your choices with your natural flow of energy

➤ You are ready to deepen your connection to your own self-awareness about what is working and what is not working in your life

➤ You want to feel lighter, more free, more balanced, and have the energy to say yes to the things you want while releasing that which isn't supporting you, and to have the grace and wisdom for the journey.

Welcome! I am honored you are here. You have taken the first step.

Let's Begin!

Note: *This journal is not intended to replace the help of a therapist, doctor, or any other healthcare professionals, but to encourage you to discover your most precious gift, you in your fullness.*

How to Use this Journal

This journal is designed to help you create intention through a practice of daily devotion using a 5-minute daily journaling practice. You may choose to set a timer for 5 minutes, or you may choose to allow yourself to journal longer. You might find that you miss a day here or there, or decide journaling works better for you at night or first thing in the morning. You get to choose what works for you. The important part is the intention that you are committed to a daily practice. You might expand this into daily meditation, prayer, movement, and/or time in nature.

Wherever you are, give yourself gratitude for your commitment and grace, and compassion for navigating life in the moments where you fall off track.

This journal includes prompts for 365 days. You can choose when and where you start. You don't have to start on a particular day or time, as long as you start. Whatever aligns with you. You will notice each month has a theme. As you flip through the pages, notice where you intuitively land, be curious about whether that is the place for you to start. If you are looking for additional support and accountability, please join our Facebook group, and journal along with the prompts listed in this book.

Journal with intention. You may notice in the beginning of your journaling practice that you begin brain-dumping, listing, or going into a story. When you notice this, take a moment to pause and reflect. Step into the space of curiosity and answer the questions as if you are redefining how you want to live. This journal is a journey in awareness and discovering the experiences that have prepared you for WHO YOU ARE BECOMING.

This Journal has 3 Sections:

1. 365 Daily Journal Prompts - for daily devotion
2. 13 New Moons each year - for monthly intention
3. 4 Seasons - for 90-day cyclical planning

Daily Devotion

I recommend you place your journal bedside, at your home office desk, or in your morning meditation space with the intention to create sacred space for this daily devotion. If you miss a day, pick up where you left off.

New Moon Monthly Planning

Plan a day and time that works each month and schedule the day in your calendar for your New Moon Planning date. This is time for you to reflect on the past month and create intention for the coming month. You may need 15 minutes or an hour for this. You might want to add the moon phases into your digital calendar, purchase a paper calendar with moon phases, or fill them in yourself. If you miss the new moon, do not worry, the important part is taking the time to reflect and redirect your intentions each month.

4 Seasons Planning

Decide on 4 Planning days for the year corresponding to each seasonal change. Many of us live according to four quarters a year in our business, taxes, or in school. Think of this as breaking down your year into 90 day increments, aligning your planning more around the seasons, length of day, temperature, and life cycles. Again, if you miss the actual Equinox or Solstice, do not worry, the important part is that you reflect at around 90 days and create new intentions around what is working and not working based on your energy flow.

Take a look at the 4 seasons and the themes and map out how your year will flow, with flexibility to adapt to life changes each season. For example, summer is a great time for activities and family travel whereas winter is a time for nourishing meals and rest. If you have big personal or professional goals, spring is the best time to plant new seeds: write a book, start a program, do a spring cleaning, or seasonally cleanse your body. Fall is the season for gathering and harvesting what you have learned and preparing for the beginning of a new year.

Create the framework for the flow of each season as you begin this journey and then commit to check in, reflect, and sometimes redesign your season.

End of the Year Reflections
At the end of this book you will find space for Gratitude, Celebrations, Notes, your Dreams, and your end-of-the-year Reflections.

Use this space to celebrate, reflect, and refer to as you plan for clarity on your alignment with your goals moving forward.

Next Steps and Resources
In the Next Steps and Resources section, we have got you covered for continued support, growth, and application of all that you learn here.

The Energetics of Cyclical Living

This journal breaks everything down into 4 major cycles. As we begin to understand the phases of life, we begin to see these four phases in many parts of our lives—divided all the way down to each day, even each hour. Women are naturally intuitive and may feel an energy shift between the moon cycles and seasons. The most fascinating is the women's menstrual or "moon" cycle broken into the 4 phases of the moon. The ovulation phase aligns with the full moon. When our 28 day "moon" or menstrual cycle is energetically aligned with the laws of nature, our menstruation phase aligns with the new moon to represent a new beginning and a need for rest. On the other hand, when we are busy and out of sync, our menstrual cycle may align closer to the full moon.

There are not only 4 phases and 4 seasons, but we can look at the cycle of life through "phases" or seasons of change as well:

4 Seasons of Life
0-25 years - Growth, Learning, Planting New Seeds, Waxing Moon, Spring
25-50 years - Connection, Career, Family, Marriage, Full Moon, Summer
50-75 years - Wisdom, Completion, Legacy, Centering, Waning Moon, Fall

75-100 years – Rest, Reflection, Transition/New Beginnings, New Moon, Winter

4 Yearly Seasons
Spring Equinox – Planting New Seeds/Growth, New Beginnings (Waxing Quarter)
Summer Solstice – Connection/Social, Long Summer Days (Full Moon)
Fall Equinox – Planning/Direction, Gather, Prepare for Change (Waning Quarter)
Winter Solstice – Rejuvenate and Reflect, Inward, Nourishment (New Moon)

4 Phases of Each Day
A 24-hour day is broken down into four 6-hour segments
00-06 am (Spring/Waxing Moon/Planning & Planting New Seeds)
06 am-12 pm or high noon (Summer/Full Moon/Connection & Productivity)
12 noon- 6 pm (Fall/Waning Moon/Harvest/Gather & Create)
6 pm-midnight (Winter/New Moon/Rest & Rejuvenate)

4 Phases of a Woman's Menstrual Cycle
1. Menstrual – New Moon, Winter, Hibernation, Rest and Rejuvenate
4. Follicular – Waxing Quarter, Spring, Energize, Preparing for Creation, Reproduction
5. Ovulation – Full Moon, Summer, Ready to Procreate, Confidence, Productivity
6. Luteal – Waning Quarter, Fall, Preparing for a New Beginning, Gathering Resources, Nesting

4 Phases of each Moon Cycle
There are 13 moons in one year. Each moon phase is 28 days

New Moon: The new moon happens when the Earth is between the moon and the sun and only the small part of the moon that we **see** is illuminated by the sun.

First Quarter: In the first quarter, we are 90 degrees away from the sun with half of the moon illuminated and growing lighter into full moon.

Full Moon: During the full moon we are 180 degrees opposite the sun and fully illuminated by the sun, which is how we can see the full moon.

Third Quarter: Halfway between the new and full moon, the sun now illuminates the other half of the moon.

When the moon phase is moving towards the new moon it is *Crescent*; when moving towards the full moon it is known as *Gibbous*.

From New Moon to Full Moon the moon becomes more full of light and is *Waxing*; the illumination of the moon appears to become fuller.

From Full Moon to New Moon is referred to as *Waning*; the illumination of the moon decreases.

The full moon energy has a greater effect on the ocean tides and we are likely to feel the energy of the moon more.

You may notice you feel more centered and grounded during a new moon.

Navigating Common Challenges

We always set out on a journey like this daily journaling with good intentions. Sometimes we stick to it 100%, but other days life happens. While the goal is to develop a daily journaling practice, if you miss a day, don't give up! Every conversation, experience, goal, and intention we set out to meet will be a path towards growth and self-reflection. You may begin to notice and witness yourself in new ways. Every cycle has and ebb and flow just like the tides. You may notice the natural expansions and contractions of life throughout this journey. You might even begin to recognize the patterns of your life in who and where you have been based on your experiences blended with moments of who you are becoming. If and when you find yourself feeling stuck or misaligned, take a moment to

Pause, Breathe, and Reflect

Ask yourself:
What pattern am I noticing? How do I feel? What is this here to teach me? What do I want to change? How do I want to feel? What do I want to experience?
What small next step am I willing to take in this moment to move towards how I want to feel and what I want to experience? What is your why? What interested you in this journal in the first place? Check out

our why and mission section for inspiration. See the Phase 1: Connect with your Why section for clarity in your personal Why.

Here are a few tips to navigate common challenges:

No Clear Connection to Your Why

Falling off track a few times here and there and stepping back on track may happen, but when you notice a pattern, it needs more intention. Take a moment to consider why you chose this journal in the first place. Is your why still valid or does it need to evolve? Is there something under the surface that maybe wasn't addressed in the beginning? Consider the bigger vision, such as your kids, family, community, big dreams, our planet, and the collective. When you say yes to you, the Universe responds with invitations and opportunities. Your life will expand into new possibilities.

Procrastination

If you feel busy or overwhelmed, it is likely the reason you began this journey. Procrastination may show up around the fear of commitment, rejection, failure, perfectionism, or a multitude of other reasons. Ask yourself, "What can I do in this moment to take the *next small step and create an intention for today?*" Get clear on what is nice to do vs. what needs to happen in life. Creating intention every day will help you gain the clarity and focus you seek to complete tasks. Set an alarm on your phone, find the support of a friend or loved one, or share this with others. When we say something out loud, we become more accountable.

Perfectionism

You will have off days. It's perfectly normal. That is the cycle of life. Give yourself permission and compassion for these days and pick back up where you left off at the next opportunity. *This is not an all or nothing experience.* It's about finding your balanced flow. The more intention you put in, the more you will receive from this experience. Trust that you are in there right place and the right time and are doing the best you can with what you have.

Low Energy
Be resourceful and aligned to your natural energy rhythms. Use the daily energy guide in your daily journal to notice patterns of where you are in the phase of your day, month, cycle, and year. There are days where you need more rest. When you give yourself permission to rest when you need it, your energy will be aligned and utilized resourcefully. The simple task of being aware of your energy levels each day will help you to align to your natural flow.

Need for Support
You may notice moments where you feel you are not getting the support you need to stay motivated. This is an opportunity to share this journaling journey with someone else. Perhaps you give this journal as a gift to a best friend, client, spouse, or colleague, and walk the journey together. We also have ways to stay connected that you can find in the Share the Love section of this journal as well as an option to join our membership circle.

Understand the Benefits vs. Cost of Staying Where You Are
If you find it difficult to stay devoted and committed to this practice, it may be an invitation for you to get clear on what it is costing you to stay were you are. Think about the missed experiences, connections, and opportunities in your relationships in your life. Imagine a year from now if that all changed. Take a moment to reconnect with your Why and remember why you began this journey in the first place.

Inconsistent Schedule

You may be a person who works on call or on a rotating schedule and find having a daily routine challenging. Give yourself permission to journal before you fall asleep or when you wake up no matter what time of day, or maybe find a consistent lunch break time to journal.

Family Obligations:

Having children, especially young ones, is an abundantly full time in life. Our sleep schedule and the needs of our family are a priority during this time. It is also important to schedule and carve out time for yourself. Perhaps you set an alarm to be up before your children get up, or journal right after they have gone to bed. Remember that an early morning routine starts the night before. Find a flow that works for you and your family in your current phase of life. As a parent, you are the foundation of the well-being and growth in your family. The best way to teach them this is by the embodiment of taking care of your own personal needs, and this means carving out time for self-care, including your journaling.

Depending on the age of your children, you may choose to involve them in your daily journaling practice. I have included my girls in such things as retreats, group meditations, and journal experiences their entire lives. The best part is that you teach them by being the example, which can create a bigger impact than telling them.

Helpful Tips: How to Stay Devoted

This journal is designed to bring a balanced flow of productivity into your life.

Begin: The best thing you can do to feel accomplished and create change is to just BEGIN. *This is your new beginning. This Journal is your New Moon.* You are planting seeds for change and just like seeds need water, light, and connection to grow, your journey will require small steps of intention.

Begin each day with an intention to create a gentle, meaningful morning routine. Allow this routine to change and evolve with you. Depending on your personality and lifestyle, you may find that five minutes is enough; others may benefit from an hour morning routine. The results and the time spent does not matter, it is the intention and how you show up that will create change in how you feel each day.

Baby Steps: If you find yourself feeling overwhelmed or frustrated ask yourself, "What is one small thing I am willing to do right now?" If you notice a pattern, become curious about the feelings and ask yourself, "Based on what I am feeling, what is it that I need in this moment in order to move forward?" Remember there is no failure, there is only growth and clarity. If you find it challenging to devote the time to yourself daily, this may be an invitation to connect more deeply with yourself and your needs.

Based on the 4 phases of each day, a well-planned day in flow with nature's cycles begins at 6 am. Of course, with the seasonal changes, there may or may not be daylight at 6 am depending on where you live. You may find rising at 6 am easier in the summer season, and your body may naturally adjust to within an hour later during winter when it is likely dark at 6 am.

Connect/Check In

You may not find every aspect of this journal resonates with you at this time. That is okay. Take what resonates for now and set the intention to try new things. Give yourself permission to try more than once. Pay attention to how you feel in the process and become curious when you notice resistance. These are often the experiences that speak to us to teach us and invite us to lean in.

Think about the following questions. I recommend you write out your answers. They may change over time, but writing them down helps with setting an intention.

What time of day do I feel will be best to complete this daily devotion?

How will I plan to initiate the monthly new moon planning? How will I remind myself?

How will I plan to expand my experience through the gratitude and celebrations section?

Find your Flow:
Find the balance between the routine of your current life and the flow of nature. Some of you may find that for your natural energy flow at this phase in your life nighttime journaling works better. Choose the time of day that works best for you. Reflect on each month's learnings and growth and then choose a time each month to create a new intention for the coming month using the New Moon Planning Pages.

Consistency is key. Many of us have heard it is 21 or 30 days to create a habit but it takes as long as it takes. Just start today and when you reach 7 days, celebrate; 21 days, celebrate again; and after 30 days you may find that it is part of your natural flow and you may begin to see and feel the results.

Remember this is about who you become along the journey, not the result. Create intention with each day, month, and season of life. Celebrate your wins, practice gratitude for all of your experiences throughout the seasons and phases of life, and most importantly enjoy the journey.

Phase I: Connect with Your Why

Our current lives are full with schedules, activities, and commitments. Take a moment to celebrate yourself or the person who gave this to you for seeing you fully and your willingness to create a devotional practice through journaling. This practice will create more clarity and intention in your life. Many members of our journaling group share that they feel more confident, more organized, have more clarity, and are in the flow with less stress since they started the journaling process. They are able to make better decisions and take aligned action.

We all have the same 24 hours in a day but we get to choose how we spend it. The purpose of this journal is to guide you to a daily intention that leads to a purpose-filled life with a bonus of clarity, fulfillment, healing, and energy alignment along the way.

"Your beliefs become your thoughts,
Your thoughts become your words,
Your words become your actions,
Your actions become your habits,
Your habits become your values,
Your values become your destiny."
Gandhi

What is your Why?

When you bought this book what was the vision you had? If you received it as a gift, what do you feel was the intention behind the person who gifted this to you? What is the experience you would like to gain?

Connecting to your WHY will set the foundation for this experience. If you find yourself falling off track, you can refer back to this page. Take a moment to close your eyes and connect with your breath. What do you want to change in your life and why do you want this change to happen? It may be personal growth, connection, or a routine... this is your time to discover and reveal your deeper WHY for your commitment, intention, and devotion to this experience.

Connect to where you are in life right now. Paint a picture in your mind: the challenges you are navigating, the habits or patterns that are not serving you, the changes you want to create, and the people in your life. Get a clear snapshot of what your life is like right now.

Take a deep breath and ask yourself, "What could like be life in 30, 60, 365 days from now if I fully commit to this journey? On a scale of 1-10 how ready am I for this change? If I am not an 8 or higher, what can I do to become more prepared for or excited about his journey? Is there someone I can share this with who will support me?"

Ask yourself, What might change for me if I fully commit to this experience? How will I feel? What changes do I want to see? How will I show up differently? What is the bigger WHY beyond my own personal daily journaling practice? How will it impact those around me?

Journal Here:

Now spend a few minutes connecting with where you are and where you want to be.

Ask yourself, How will my life look if I stay where I am? What happens if I do not commit to this? What am I missing out on and how will that make me feel? Who will be missing out on the version of me I can become if I complete this? How does that make me feel?

Journal Here:

What do I believe is standing in the way of my becoming a person who can fully commit to this experience? What challenges do I face?

Journal Here:

(blank journaling box)

Who do I become when I fall off track? How do I show up?
Who can I call on for support when I get off track? How can I maintain a balance of compassion and self-responsibility when it comes to staying on track?

Journal Here:

(blank journaling box)

What is a reasonable goal I am willing to create today around this experience?

Who can I share this goal and my planned celebration with? How will I celebrate when I reach goals around my commitment to this?"

Journal Here:

Devotion Statement

Repeat this to yourself, out loud: I am willing, able, and excited for this daily devotion journaling experience. I am committed to my intention to learn from and use this as a tool to living with a daily devotional practice and cyclical monthly intention-setting. I recognize that some days will be harder than others and I will give myself grace for the expansions and contractions of life. I will stay in the flow of compassion and self-responsibility to navigate the ebb and flow of life. I will set the intention to wake up each day with heart-centered purpose and commitment to connect with my daily journaling practice. If I fall off track, I will call on the support of loved ones listed here who want to see me succeed and to fulfill this mission just as much as I want to. I am going to give it my best!

Please add anything you wish to this statement here:

_____

_____

_____

_____

_____

_____

Signature   Date

Phase II: Daily Devotion

How to Use this Section:

1. Start today

2. Commit to at least 30 days

3. Create a routine

4. Journal. Reflect with Gratitude, End with a Positive Reframe/ Affirmation/Intention

5. Find your rhythm and flow

6. Share with others

7. Celebrate Wins

January

"Your sacred space is where you can find yourself again and again."
—Joseph Campbell

Date_____ Time_____

Exhausted · Overwhelm · Focused · Centered · High Vibin'

What is my goal or intention (my WHY) around joining this devotional journaling experience? What do I hope to learn or gain from this?

Today's Positive Affirmation/Intention

Date_____ Time_____

Exhausted · Overwhelm · Focused · Centered · High Vibin'

What is the best time of the day for me to carve out to commit to this journaling experience? How much time am I willing to commit to?

Today's Positive Affirmation/Intention

Date_____ Time_____

Exhausted · Overwhelm · Focused · Centered · High Vibin'

Why is now a good time for me to commit to myself through a small daily practice of journaling?

Today's Positive Affirmation/Intention

Date_____ Time_____

Exhausted · Overwhelm · Focused · Centered · High Vibin'

What happens when I fall off track on my daily commitment? What does it say about me? How do I feel? What happens next?

Today's Positive Affirmation/Intention

Date_____ Time_____

Exhausted · Overwhelm · Focused · Centered · High Vibin'

Who in my life can I count on to support me when I fall off track and how?

Today's Positive Affirmation/Intention

34

Date_____ Time_____

Exhausted · Overwhelm · Focused · Centered · High Vibin'

What is one small action I can take today aligned with my goals for this month and my journaling practice? What do I need to believe about myself in order to take this one small aligned action step?

Today's Positive Affirmation/Intention

Date_____ Time_____

Exhausted · Overwhelm · Focused · Centered · High Vibin'

What is my one-word intention for this year? What does it mean to me? How do I want to show up?

Today's Positive Affirmation/Intention

Date_____ Time_____

Exhausted · Overwhelm · Focused · Centered · High Vibin'

What feeling or emotion do I believe is getting in the way of how I want to show up when it comes to my one-word intention for this year?

Today's Positive Affirmation/Intention

Date_____ Time_____

Exhausted · Overwhelm · Focused · Centered · High Vibin'

What are my fears around my intentions, goals, and dreams?

Today's Positive Affirmation/Intention

Date_____ Time_____

Exhausted · Overwhelm · Focused · Centered · High Vibin'

What challenges am I faced with around my goals and intentions and how do I feel these challenges are holding me back?

Today's Positive Affirmation/Intention

Date_____ Time_____

Exhausted · Overwhelm · Focused · Centered · High Vibin'

What do I feel the top emotional, physical, or mental bocks are from achieving and living how I want?

Today's Positive Affirmation/Intention

Date_____ Time_____

Exhausted · Overwhelm · Focused · Centered · High Vibin'

Reflect on the past year. What challenges did I overcome that I can celebrate myself for?

Today's Positive Affirmation/Intention

Date_____ Time_____

Exhausted · Overwhelm · Focused · Centered · High Vibin'

Looking back on those challenges. What did I learn? How did I grow?
What am I no longer available for?

Today's Positive Affirmation/Intention

Date_____ Time_____

Exhausted · Overwhelm · Focused · Centered · High Vibin'

What positive changes do I want to create in my life for this year and why do these matter?

Today's Positive Affirmation/Intention

Date_____ Time_____

Exhausted · Overwhelm · Focused · Centered · High Vibin'

What area of my life (mental, physical, spiritual, financial, relationship, career, emotional) do I need the most support in and why?

Today's Positive Affirmation/Intention

Date_____ Time_____

Exhausted · Overwhelm · Focused · Centered · High Vibin'

What change do I want to create in my physical well-being and why does this matter?

Today's Positive Affirmation/Intention

Date_____ Time_____

Exhausted · Overwhelm · Focused · Centered · High Vibin'

What change do I want to create in my mental well-being and why does this matter?

Today's Positive Affirmation/Intention

Date_____ Time_____

Exhausted · Overwhelm · Focused · Centered · High Vibin'

What change do I want to create on my spiritual path and why does this matter?

Today's Positive Affirmation/Intention

47

Date_____ Time_____

Exhausted · Overwhelm · Focused · Centered · High Vibin'

What change do I want to create around my emotional well-being and why does this matter?

Today's Positive Affirmation/Intention

48

Date_____ Time_____

Exhausted · Overwhelm · Focused · Centered · High Vibin'

How aligned are the actions I take in life with the goals I have for myself? Do my calendar (time) and money spent reflect alignment with what I want and need?

Today's Positive Affirmation/Intention

Date_____ Time_____

Exhausted · Overwhelm · Focused · Centered · High Vibin'

What will it look like If I chose to trust more in my life? How would I feel, what would I do?

Today's Positive Affirmation/Intention

Date_____ Time_____

Exhausted · Overwhelm · Focused · Centered · High Vibin'

What would I act on if I had more confidence in my life? What would I do differently?

Today's Positive Affirmation/Intention

Date_____ Time_____

Exhausted · Overwhelm · Focused · Centered · High Vibin'

What steps have I already taken in life that sets me up to believe I can achieve my goals?

Today's Positive Affirmation/Intention

Date_____ Time_____

Exhausted · Overwhelm · Focused · Centered · High Vibin'

What do I believe is keeping me from achieving what I want? How is this impacting me?

Today's Positive Affirmation/Intention

Date_____ Time_____

Exhausted · Overwhelm · Focused · Centered · High Vibin'

What have I learned so far about what matters to me and how I am showing up in life?

Today's Positive Affirmation/Intention

Date_____ Time_____

Exhausted · Overwhelm · Focused · Centered · High Vibin'

What is my relationship with time? Do I have enough? Is it plentiful?

Today's Positive Affirmation/Intention

Date_____ Time_____

Exhausted · Overwhelm · Focused · Centered · High Vibin'

What top 3 challenges come up around my beliefs around time management? Do I prioritize what matters most? How are these challenges and beliefs holding me back from creating the life I want?

Today's Positive Affirmation/Intention

Date_____ Time_____

Exhausted · Overwhelm · Focused · Centered · High Vibin'

What do I desire more time for and why? How can I become curious about a commitment to carving this out in my calendar?

Today's Positive Affirmation/Intention

Date_____ Time_____

Exhausted · Overwhelm · Focused · Centered · High Vibin'

How do I feel about the amount of time I have now and the time I have left in my life? Am I living the life I want? Is there more for me?

Today's Positive Affirmation/Intention

Date_____ Time_____

Exhausted · Overwhelm · Focused · Centered · High Vibin'

How am I showing up in my daily life as it relates to the use of my time? Am I spending my time aligned with what matters most? What do I want to change?

Today's Positive Affirmation/Intention

Date_____ Time_____

Exhausted · Overwhelm · Focused · Centered · High Vibin'

What is my relationship to energy? Do I have enough? Is it high? Low and anxious? Grounded?

Today's Positive Affirmation/Intention

February

"There are no problems, only opportunities for growth."
—Rebbetzin Dena Weinberg:

Date_____ Time_____

Exhausted · Overwhelm · Focused · Centered · High Vibin'

What am I ready to prioritize in my life based on my beliefs around time and energy so that I can show up the way I want to?

Today's Positive Affirmation/Intention

Date_____ Time_____

Exhausted · Overwhelm · Focused · Centered · High Vibin'

What do I desire more energy for in life and why?

Today's Positive Affirmation/Intention

Date_____ Time_____

Exhausted · Overwhelm · Focused · Centered · High Vibin'

When I think of my time and energy, are there things I am missing out on? Places to go, things to do, people to reach out to or spend more time with?

Today's Positive Affirmation/Intention

64

Date_____ Time_____

Exhausted · Overwhelm · Focused · Centered · High Vibin'

How am I showing up in my daily life as it relates to my energy levels?

Today's Positive Affirmation/Intention

Date_____ Time_____

Exhausted · Overwhelm · Focused · Centered · High Vibin'

How do my loved ones see that I use my time and energy? What would they say? What do they see?

Today's Positive Affirmation/Intention

Date_____ Time_____

Exhausted · Overwhelm · Focused · Centered · High Vibin'

Am I present and intentional with my time and energy? If so, list are the ways; if not, what keeps me from that?

Today's Positive Affirmation/Intention

Date_____ Time_____

Exhausted · Overwhelm · Focused · Centered · High Vibin'

What are 3 energy drains in my life that need releasing?

Today's Positive Affirmation/Intention

Date_____ Time_____

Exhausted · Overwhelm · Focused · Centered · High Vibin'

What is one area in my life I can make a request around receiving support when it comes to managing my time and energy?

Today's Positive Affirmation/Intention

Date_____ Time_____

Exhausted · Overwhelm · Focused · Centered · High Vibin'

An ideal 24-hour day.... If I were to create my ideal 24-hour day, this is what it would look like and how I would feel...

Today's Positive Affirmation/Intention

Date_____ Time_____

Exhausted · Overwhelm · Focused · Centered · High Vibin'

Today I am going to commit to a brain dump exercise and use this time to list all the things I think I have to do. When I am done, I will look for areas I can ask for support. I will also note and mark things that are actually a priority that are aligned with my goals.

Today's Positive Affirmation/Intention

Date_____ Time_____

Exhausted · Overwhelm · Focused · Centered · High Vibin'

Today's Positive Affirmation/Intention

Date_____ Time_____

Exhausted · Overwhelm · Focused · Centered · High Vibin'

What have I leaned about my relationship to sacred space, time, energy?

Today's Positive Affirmation/Intention

Date_____ Time_____

Exhausted · Overwhelm · Focused · Centered · High Vibin'

When I think about what I want in life and I notice my beliefs around time, energy, and support, what limiting beliefs, challenges, doubts, or fears do I notice?

Today's Positive Affirmation/Intention

Date_____ Time_____

Exhausted · Overwhelm · Focused · Centered · High Vibin'

When I look at my beliefs, challenges, and fears, what other areas of my life do I notice them showing up?

Today's Positive Affirmation/Intention

Date_____ Time_____

Exhausted · Overwhelm · Focused · Centered · High Vibin'

When I think about my doubts, fears, and limiting beliefs, how do I feel?

Today's Positive Affirmation/Intention

Date_____ Time_____

Exhausted · Overwhelm · Focused · Centered · High Vibin'

What sabotaging beliefs am I starting to notice in my life that have been a repeating pattern? When did this first begin? How old was I? What was the experience? Who was there?

Today's Positive Affirmation/Intention

Date_____ Time_____

Exhausted · Overwhelm · Focused · Centered · High Vibin'

When I think about my limiting beliefs, how did I feel and what need did I have that wasn't met?

Today's Positive Affirmation/Intention

Date_____ Time_____

Exhausted · Overwhelm · Focused · Centered · High Vibin'

When I think about my fears, doubts, and sabotaging patterns, where is this impacting me in my current life?

Today's Positive Affirmation/Intention

Date_____ Time_____

Exhausted · Overwhelm · Focused · Centered · High Vibin'

When I think about my fears, doubts, and sabotaging patterns, what do I choose to forgive?

Today's Positive Affirmation/Intention

Date_____ Time_____

Exhausted · Overwhelm · Focused · Centered · High Vibin'

When I think about my fears, doubts, and sabotaging patterns, what story needs to be released?

Today's Positive Affirmation/Intention

Date_____ Time_____

Exhausted · Overwhelm · Focused · Centered · High Vibin'

When I think about my fears, doubts, and sabotaging patterns, what thoughts need to be released?

Today's Positive Affirmation/Intention

Date_____ Time_____

Exhausted · Overwhelm · Focused · Centered · High Vibin'

When I think about my fears, doubts, and sabotaging patterns, what emotions or feelings need to be released? Anything else?

Today's Positive Affirmation/Intention

Date_____ Time_____

Exhausted · Overwhelm · Focused · Centered · High Vibin'

When I think of what I want to release, what is it costing me to stay where I am? Who is missing out on the real me if I stay stuck?

Today's Positive Affirmation/Intention

Date_____ Time_____

Exhausted · Overwhelm · Focused · Centered · High Vibin'

What am I willing to accept about myself and my experiences around what I have learned about myself in the ways in which I show up around my fears, doubts, and sabotaging patterns?

Today's Positive Affirmation/Intention

Date_____ Time_____

Exhausted · Overwhelm · Focused · Centered · High Vibin'

What are 3 ways I can look back at these challenging experiences and see how I grew from them? What is a positive way I can see these experiences and how they have made me the person I am today?

Today's Positive Affirmation/Intention

Date_____ Time_____

Exhausted · Overwhelm · Focused · Centered · High Vibin'

What beliefs do I want to choose to believe moving forward? What is an empowering way I can rewrite my story?

Today's Positive Affirmation/Intention

Date_____ Time_____

Exhausted · Overwhelm · Focused · Centered · High Vibin'

How will I feel when I create these new empowering beliefs?

Today's Positive Affirmation/Intention

Date_____ Time_____

Exhausted · Overwhelm · Focused · Centered · High Vibin'

How will my loved ones and the world around me respond to these new empowering beliefs?

Today's Positive Affirmation/Intention

March

"To love oneself is the beginning of a life-long romance."
—Oscar Wilde

Date_____ Time_____

Exhausted · Overwhelm · Focused · Centered · High Vibin'

What have I learned from being willing to shift the story around my new beliefs?

Today's Positive Affirmation/Intention

Date_____ Time_____

Exhausted · Overwhelm · Focused · Centered · High Vibin'

What breakthrough can I celebrate myself for this week?

Today's Positive Affirmation/Intention

Date_____ Time_____

Exhausted · Overwhelm · Focused · Centered · High Vibin'

What am I hopeful about this month?

Today's Positive Affirmation/Intention

Date_____ Time_____

Exhausted · Overwhelm · Focused · Centered · High Vibin'

What fears come up around achieving my hopes and dreams and goals this month?

Today's Positive Affirmation/Intention

Date_____ Time_____

Exhausted · Overwhelm · Focused · Centered · High Vibin'

What actions have I taken to align myself in my values and get closer to achieving my goals?

Today's Positive Affirmation/Intention

Date_____ Time_____

Exhausted · Overwhelm · Focused · Centered · High Vibin'

Today I am writing a letter to myself about my goals and intentions for this month. I am also going to share about my dreams and desires in life. I am going to let myself dream.

Today's Positive Affirmation/Intention

Date_____ Time_____

Exhausted · Overwhelm · Focused · Centered · High Vibin'

As I look back on my dreams and goals, sometimes I notice stories of doubt, fear, and reasons why they can't or won't happen. What story am I still carrying around?

Today's Positive Affirmation/Intention

Date_____ Time_____

Exhausted · Overwhelm · Focused · Centered · High Vibin'

What is an emotional response I had today or this week that I am proud of?

Today's Positive Affirmation/Intention

Date_____ Time_____

Exhausted · Overwhelm · Focused · Centered · High Vibin'

How have I set my future self up for success today?

Today's Positive Affirmation/Intention

Date_____ Time_____

Exhausted · Overwhelm · Focused · Centered · High Vibin'

How have I shown myself love and respect today? How have I shown others?

Today's Positive Affirmation/Intention

Date_____ Time_____

Exhausted · Overwhelm · Focused · Centered · High Vibin'

What memorable moments have I experienced recently. Who was I with? What was I doing? How did I feel?

Today's Positive Affirmation/Intention

Date_____ Time_____

Exhausted · Overwhelm · Focused · Centered · High Vibin'

What quality or characteristic about myself am I grateful for today and why?

Today's Positive Affirmation/Intention

Date_____ Time_____

Exhausted · Overwhelm · Focused · Centered · High Vibin'

What quality or characteristic do I love about myself that I want to share more of with others and why?

Today's Positive Affirmation/Intention

Date_____ Time_____

Exhausted · Overwhelm · Focused · Centered · High Vibin'

How will others respond to me showing up in these parts of myself that I love?

Today's Positive Affirmation/Intention

Date_____ Time_____

Exhausted · Overwhelm · Focused · Centered · High Vibin'

What is my current relationship to the idea of self love or self care?
Do I need more? Do I currently have a routine? Is there a routine I am
willing to create?

Today's Positive Affirmation/Intention

Date_____ Time_____

Exhausted · Overwhelm · Focused · Centered · High Vibin'

What is my story about what it means for me to take care of myself or to love myself? Where did it come from? How do I feel about it?

Today's Positive Affirmation/Intention

Date_____ Time_____

Exhausted · Overwhelm · Focused · Centered · High Vibin'

Is there an affirmation or a quote that I love around self love that I would like to embody? If I don't have one, I will find one or come up with one and I will share it here. Why do I love this affirmation or quote?

Today's Positive Affirmation/Intention

Date_____ Time_____

Exhausted · Overwhelm · Focused · Centered · High Vibin'

What small change am I willing to create to embody an affirmation or quote that I love about myself love today? How will it look and feel differently?

Today's Positive Affirmation/Intention

Date_____ Time_____

Exhausted · Overwhelm · Focused · Centered · High Vibin'

What is my idea of self care and self love? What actions do I take?
How does it make me feel?

Today's Positive Affirmation/Intention

Date_____ Time_____

Exhausted · Overwhelm · Focused · Centered · High Vibin'

What are the ways I take actions of self love? What do I love about them?

Today's Positive Affirmation/Intention

Date_____ Time_____

Exhausted · Overwhelm · Focused · Centered · High Vibin'

What are the ways I embody self love? How does it make me feel?
What do I notice is different in the actions of self care and the embodiment of self love?

Today's Positive Affirmation/Intention

Date_____ Time_____

Exhausted · Overwhelm · Focused · Centered · High Vibin'

How do I feel when I take time to care for myself?

Today's Positive Affirmation/Intention

Date_____ Time_____

Exhausted · Overwhelm · Focused · Centered · High Vibin'

How do others respond when I take time to care for myself?

Today's Positive Affirmation/Intention

Date_____ Time_____

Exhausted · Overwhelm · Focused · Centered · High Vibin'

If I am being honest, how much stress and overwhelm do I experience in life? What are the major areas of stress? How do I show up when I am stressed?

Today's Positive Affirmation/Intention

Date_____ Time_____

Exhausted · Overwhelm · Focused · Centered · High Vibin'

What do I believe the top stressors are in my life and why? How do they impact my life?

Today's Positive Affirmation/Intention

Date_____ Time_____

Exhausted · Overwhelm · Focused · Centered · High Vibin'

How do I respond to stress in my life? Do I avoid? Freeze? Get angry?
What do I notice about my response to stress?

Today's Positive Affirmation/Intention

Date_____ Time_____

Exhausted · Overwhelm · Focused · Centered · High Vibin'

What are the tools I have to respond to stressful situations? How confident am I that I can use these tools when I notice stress in my life?

Today's Positive Affirmation/Intention

Date_____ Time_____

Exhausted · Overwhelm · Focused · Centered · High Vibin'

What support can I ask for around my stress levels? Where and who?

Today's Positive Affirmation/Intention

Date_____ Time_____

Exhausted · Overwhelm · Focused · Centered · High Vibin'

What are 1-3 small actions I can take today to reduce stress in my life? Why does this matter to me? How will it affect me and others around me?

Today's Positive Affirmation/Intention

Date_____ Time_____

Exhausted · Overwhelm · Focused · Centered · High Vibin'

What is an area of my life where I experience stress that I would like to create a healthy boundary around? What will happen if I do this? Who will it effect? What will change? How will I and others feel about this?

Today's Positive Affirmation/Intention

Date_____ Time_____

Exhausted · Overwhelm · Focused · Centered · High Vibin'

What story have I been carrying around that I am willing to forgive my-self for in this moment? How will I feel when I have compassion for the version of me that played it safe in my habitual pattern of this story?

Today's Positive Affirmation/Intention

April

"Knowing others is intelligence;
knowing yourself is true wisdom.
Mastering others is strength;
mastering yourself is true power."
—Lao Tzu, Tao Te Ching

Date_____ Time_____

Exhausted · Overwhelm · Focused · Centered · High Vibin'

How do I feel about my overall state of well-being?

Today's Positive Affirmation/Intention

Date_____ Time_____

Exhausted · Overwhelm · Focused · Centered · High Vibin'

What is the story I notice around my health and well-being?

Today's Positive Affirmation/Intention

Date_____ Time_____

Exhausted · Overwhelm · Focused · Centered · High Vibin'

What part of my well-being is needing attention? Physical? Mental?
Emotional? Spiritual? Why? Why does this matter to me?

Today's Positive Affirmation/Intention

Date_____ Time_____

Exhausted · Overwhelm · Focused · Centered · High Vibin'

How do I feel about the way I nourish my body? What is my relationship to food? Do I eat healthily?

Today's Positive Affirmation/Intention

Date_____ Time_____

Exhausted · Overwhelm · Focused · Centered · High Vibin'

What do I notice about the way I was raised that impacts my food choices or my relationship to my food and how do I feel about it? Do I need to forgive someone?

Today's Positive Affirmation/Intention

Date_____ Time_____

Exhausted · Overwhelm · Focused · Centered · High Vibin'

What challenges have I noticed throughout my life when it comes to
making healthy choices with food and nutrition?

Today's Positive Affirmation/Intention

Date_____ Time_____

Exhausted · Overwhelm · Focused · Centered · High Vibin'

What are my top 3 goals around my health and well-being for this year? Who can support me? Why do these matter?

Today's Positive Affirmation/Intention

Date_____ Time_____

Exhausted · Overwhelm · Focused · Centered · High Vibin'

How will I feel when I accomplish my goals around my health and well-being? What will happen if I don't prioritize my health?

Today's Positive Affirmation/Intention

Date_____ Time_____

Exhausted · Overwhelm · Focused · Centered · High Vibin'

Who can I ask to support me on my goals around my health and well-being and what will it look like?

Today's Positive Affirmation/Intention

Date_____ Time_____

Exhausted · Overwhelm · Focused · Centered · High Vibin'

What symptoms do I have that I have gotten used to that I wish were not there? Brain fog? Low energy? Skin rashes? Body aches? Allergies? Mood swings? How are these impacting my life?

Today's Positive Affirmation/Intention

Date_____ Time_____

Exhausted · Overwhelm · Focused · Centered · High Vibin'

When it comes to nutrition and nourishing myself I feel, what 3 challenges come up for me? How do I feel about this?

Today's Positive Affirmation/Intention

Date_____ Time_____

Exhausted · Overwhelm · Focused · Centered · High Vibin'

When it comes to meal planning or prepping, I notice I feel...

Today's Positive Affirmation/Intention

Date_____ Time_____

Exhausted · Overwhelm · Focused · Centered · High Vibin'

If I were to commit to eating healthier this year, what would that mean for me and what would that look like?

Today's Positive Affirmation/Intention

Date_____ Time_____

Exhausted · Overwhelm · Focused · Centered · High Vibin'

The most challenging time of the day for me when it comes to eating healthily is...

Today's Positive Affirmation/Intention

Date_____ Time_____

Exhausted · Overwhelm · Focused · Centered · High Vibin'

The most challenging emotions that come up for me around my relationship to food are...

Today's Positive Affirmation/Intention

138

Date_____ Time_____

Exhausted · Overwhelm · Focused · Centered · High Vibin'

What am I willing to welcome in as a form on nourishment in my life to support my well-being?

Today's Positive Affirmation/Intention

Date_____ Time_____

Exhausted · Overwhelm · Focused · Centered · High Vibin'

What have I already done in my life that sets me up for success around creating an intention for healthy nourishment and well-being in my life?

Today's Positive Affirmation/Intention

Date_____ Time_____

Exhausted · Overwhelm · Focused · Centered · High Vibin'

What do I need to learn more about so that I can properly nourish my body and feel my best every day?

Today's Positive Affirmation/Intention

Date_____ Time_____

Exhausted · Overwhelm · Focused · Centered · High Vibin'

Who do I know, or what resource do I have that I am willing to commit to that will help me improve my eating habits, relationship to food, and my well-being?

Today's Positive Affirmation/Intention

Date_____ Time_____

Exhausted · Overwhelm · Focused · Centered · High Vibin'

What goal or intention am I willing to create today around my health?

Today's Positive Affirmation/Intention

Date_____ Time_____

Exhausted · Overwhelm · Focused · Centered · High Vibin'

What am I most excited about when it comes to how I will feel around prioritizing my health and well-being?

Today's Positive Affirmation/Intention

Date_____ Time_____

Exhausted · Overwhelm · Focused · Centered · High Vibin'

What areas of my life do I notice I have more energy, am more productive, and feel better about myself when I take care of myself?

Today's Positive Affirmation/Intention

Date_____ Time_____

Exhausted · Overwhelm · Focused · Centered · High Vibin'

What flavors and foods do I love and why?

Today's Positive Affirmation/Intention

Date_____ Time_____

Exhausted · Overwhelm · Focused · Centered · High Vibin'

What do I notice about the habits I have when it comes to a healthy lifestyle? Do I make time for it? Do I value it?

Today's Positive Affirmation/Intention

Date_____ Time_____

Exhausted · Overwhelm · Focused · Centered · High Vibin'

What is one small way that I can be more mindful about the way I nourish myself?

Today's Positive Affirmation/Intention

Date_____ Time_____

Exhausted · Overwhelm · Focused · Centered · High Vibin'

What is one unhealthy habit I am ready to let go of that I know is not serving me? Maybe even just for a month? How will I feel about it after I have done this?

Today's Positive Affirmation/Intention

Date_____ Time_____

Exhausted · Overwhelm · Focused · Centered · High Vibin'

What challenges do I notice may come up around creating new healthier habits in my life?

Today's Positive Affirmation/Intention

Date_____ Time_____

Exhausted · Overwhelm · Focused · Centered · High Vibin'

Who do I know that can support me in living a healthier lifestyle, committing to healthier foods, and making time for my well-being?

Today's Positive Affirmation/Intention

Date_____ Time_____

Exhausted · Overwhelm · Focused · Centered · High Vibin'

What have I learned about myself by becoming more aware of the
way I choose to nourish myself?

Today's Positive Affirmation/Intention

Date_____ Time_____

Exhausted · Overwhelm · Focused · Centered · High Vibin'

What am I ready to create more of in my life based on what I have learned about myself this month?

Today's Positive Affirmation/Intention

May

"Life is from the inside out. When you shift on the inside,
life shifts on the outside."
—Kamal Ravikant

Date_____ Time_____

Exhausted · Overwhelm · Focused · Centered · High Vibin'

What am I excited about and hopeful for this month?

Today's Positive Affirmation/Intention

Date_____ Time_____

Exhausted · Overwhelm · Focused · Centered · High Vibin'

What aligned action am I willing to take towards my goals and intentions for this month?

Today's Positive Affirmation/Intention

Date_____ Time_____

Exhausted · Overwhelm · Focused · Centered · High Vibin'

What is my current relationship to movement and exercise?

Today's Positive Affirmation/Intention

Date_____ Time_____

Exhausted · Overwhelm · Focused · Centered · High Vibin'

What is my current relationship to my physical body?

Today's Positive Affirmation/Intention

Date_____ Time_____

Exhausted · Overwhelm · Focused · Centered · High Vibin'

What thoughts and judgments do I notice when I think about my current relationship to my body?

Today's Positive Affirmation/Intention

Date_____ Time_____

Exhausted · Overwhelm · Focused · Centered · High Vibin'

What challenges have I overcome around health and relationship to my physical body?

Today's Positive Affirmation/Intention

Date_____ Time_____

Exhausted · Overwhelm · Focused · Centered · High Vibin'

What value do I put on exercise and movement in my life? Do I take part in this daily? Weekly?

Today's Positive Affirmation/Intention

Date_____ Time_____

Exhausted · Overwhelm · Focused · Centered · High Vibin'

What forms of movement do I enjoy and why? No movement is too small. If I am not exercising or moving, what do I believe is keeping me from this? Do I want to exercise and move more? Is there someone who can help me?

Today's Positive Affirmation/Intention

Date_____ Time_____

Exhausted · Overwhelm · Focused · Centered · High Vibin'

What are challenges that show up around committing to physical exercise and movement?

Today's Positive Affirmation/Intention

164

Date_____ Time_____

Exhausted · Overwhelm · Focused · Centered · High Vibin'

What do I believe are the benefits of movement or exercise in my body?

Today's Positive Affirmation/Intention

Date_____ Time_____

Exhausted · Overwhelm · Focused · Centered · High Vibin'

Do I feel I have enough energy for movement? Do I feel I know how to fuel my body properly and remained balanced during my exercise routine? If not, is there a resource or someone who can support me?

Today's Positive Affirmation/Intention

Date_____ Time_____

Exhausted · Overwhelm · Focused · Centered · High Vibin'

How connected do I feel to my physical body? Am I in tune? Do I listen to its needs around food, movement, preventing injuries, and to my body wisdom? If not, is there someone who can support me?

Today's Positive Affirmation/Intention

Date_____ Time_____

Exhausted · Overwhelm · Focused · Centered · High Vibin'

What patterns or beliefs do I notice around my physical body and trusting it to remain strong and healthy? Do I trust my body?

Today's Positive Affirmation/Intention

Date_____ Time_____

Exhausted · Overwhelm · Focused · Centered · High Vibin'

What is a story I am willing to accept, acknowledge, and release around the health of my physical body based on my life experiences? How will this impact me moving forward?

Today's Positive Affirmation/Intention

Date_____ Time_____

Exhausted · Overwhelm · Focused · Centered · High Vibin'

What is a story I am willing to release around what it takes or means to be healthy that is no longer serving me? How will this impact me moving forward?

Today's Positive Affirmation/Intention

Date_____ Time_____

Exhausted · Overwhelm · Focused · Centered · High Vibin'

What is my idea of healthy? Where did this come from? How do I feel about it?

Today's Positive Affirmation/Intention

Date_____ Time_____

Exhausted · Overwhelm · Focused · Centered · High Vibin'

What are some physical activities that I enjoy doing and what do I love about them?

Today's Positive Affirmation/Intention

Date_____ Time_____

Exhausted · Overwhelm · Focused · Centered · High Vibin'

What are the challenges that come up around creating more time for physical activity in my life?

Today's Positive Affirmation/Intention

Date_____ Time_____

Exhausted · Overwhelm · Focused · Centered · High Vibin'

How are these challenges holding me back from feeling better about my health and well-being in my life?

Today's Positive Affirmation/Intention

Date_____ Time_____

Exhausted · Overwhelm · Focused · Centered · High Vibin'

What am I willing to commit to this week around physical activity and who can I share with to support me?

Today's Positive Affirmation/Intention

Date_____ Time_____

Exhausted · Overwhelm · Focused · Centered · High Vibin'

What physical activities bring me joy? Why do they bring me joy?

Today's Positive Affirmation/Intention

Date_____ Time_____

Exhausted · Overwhelm · Focused · Centered · High Vibin'

How often do I participate in the physical activities that bring me joy? How do I feel about this?

Today's Positive Affirmation/Intention

177

Date_____ Time_____

Exhausted · Overwhelm · Focused · Centered · High Vibin'

What story do I notice around movement in my body that keeps me from moving in a way that feels good for me?

Today's Positive Affirmation/Intention

178

Date_____ Time_____

Exhausted · Overwhelm · Focused · Centered · High Vibin'

What insecurities or doubts do I notice show up when it comes to trying different ways to exercise and move?

Today's Positive Affirmation/Intention

Date_____ Time_____

Exhausted · Overwhelm · Focused · Centered · High Vibin'

What doubts and insecurities am I willing to work through so that I can commit to the moment and exercise for my health that I want for myself?

Today's Positive Affirmation/Intention

Date_____ Time_____

Exhausted · Overwhelm · Focused · Centered · High Vibin'

Why is it important for me to keep moving?

Today's Positive Affirmation/Intention

Date_____ Time_____

Exhausted · Overwhelm · Focused · Centered · High Vibin'

What happens if I stop movement in my life, if I stop exercising, taking walks, or taking part in activities I love, and how do I feel about it?

Today's Positive Affirmation/Intention

Date_____ Time_____

Exhausted · Overwhelm · Focused · Centered · High Vibin'

What is a new form of movement I have always wanted to try but been afraid to try? How can I take part in this? What doubts am I ready to release around this?

Today's Positive Affirmation/Intention

Date_____ Time_____

Exhausted · Overwhelm · Focused · Centered · High Vibin'

When I begin moving in my body, when I develop a healthy relationship to my body, I notice that I feel... and that makes me feel... about myself. Because of this I am willing to commit to... for this week or month, and I will call on... to help me

Today's Positive Affirmation/Intention

Date_____ Time_____

Exhausted · Overwhelm · Focused · Centered · High Vibin'

Today I am celebrating myself for...

Today's Positive Affirmation/Intention

Date_____ Time_____

Exhausted · Overwhelm · Focused · Centered · High Vibin'

I have learned so many things about my relationship to my body and movement and health. My top 3 takeaways are...

Today's Positive Affirmation/Intention

June

"You were given this life because you are strong enough to live it."
—unknown.

Date_____ Time_____

Exhausted · Overwhelm · Focused · Centered · High Vibin'

What am I excited about and hopeful for this month?

Today's Positive Affirmation/Intention

Date_____ Time_____

Exhausted · Overwhelm · Focused · Centered · High Vibin'

What aligned action am I willing to take towards my goals and intentions for this month?

Today's Positive Affirmation/Intention

Date_____ Time_____

Exhausted · Overwhelm · Focused · Centered · High Vibin'

What is my relationship to joy?

Today's Positive Affirmation/Intention

Date_____ Time_____

Exhausted · Overwhelm · Focused · Centered · High Vibin'

What stories do I notice when it comes to people who are happy or joyful?

Today's Positive Affirmation/Intention

Date_____ Time_____

Exhausted · Overwhelm · Focused · Centered · High Vibin'

How many times a week do I experience joy?

Today's Positive Affirmation/Intention

Date_____ Time_____

Exhausted · Overwhelm · Focused · Centered · High Vibin'

What does joy feel like to me? Where do I feel it in my body and what are the memories associated with it?

Today's Positive Affirmation/Intention

Date_____ Time_____

Exhausted · Overwhelm · Focused · Centered · High Vibin'

If I were to meet my joyful inner child, what would she be like? What does she do and what makes her happy?

Today's Positive Affirmation/Intention

Date_____ Time_____

Exhausted · Overwhelm · Focused · Centered · High Vibin'

Do you need to schedule joy or do you experience it spontaneously in the moment?

Today's Positive Affirmation/Intention

Date_____ Time_____

Exhausted · Overwhelm · Focused · Centered · High Vibin'

Who are the 5 people you spend the most time with? Share a few traits about each of them. Do these people reflect positive or negative emotions in you?

Today's Positive Affirmation/Intention

Date_____ Time_____

Exhausted · Overwhelm · Focused · Centered · High Vibin'

Stress is the enemy of joy. What causes me stress and how can I respond in a healthier way?

Today's Positive Affirmation/Intention

Date_____ Time_____

Exhausted · Overwhelm · Focused · Centered · High Vibin'

Comparison is an enemy of joy. What ways do I compare myself to others that makes me feel unhappy and how am I willing to shift this?

Today's Positive Affirmation/Intention

Date_____ Time_____

Exhausted · Overwhelm · Focused · Centered · High Vibin'

If I were to live as the best version of myself today, what would that be?

Today's Positive Affirmation/Intention

Date_____ Time_____

Exhausted · Overwhelm · Focused · Centered · High Vibin'

Who is one person I can give extra love, care, and attention to today?

Today's Positive Affirmation/Intention

Date_____ Time_____

Exhausted · Overwhelm · Focused · Centered · High Vibin'

What is an accomplishment I can celebrate today?

Today's Positive Affirmation/Intention

Date_____ Time_____

Exhausted · Overwhelm · Focused · Centered · High Vibin'

What can I celebrate in this moment as I journal? What does it feel like in my body?

Today's Positive Affirmation/Intention

Date_____ Time_____

Exhausted · Overwhelm · Focused · Centered · High Vibin'

What is an area of my life that I can create more enthusiasm and joy around?

Today's Positive Affirmation/Intention

Date_____ Time_____

Exhausted · Overwhelm · Focused · Centered · High Vibin'

What is an area of life that I can create more peace and calm around?

Today's Positive Affirmation/Intention

Date_____ Time_____

Exhausted · Overwhelm · Focused · Centered · High Vibin'

Who is one person in my life who creates a positive impact in my life that I want to spend more time with?

Today's Positive Affirmation/Intention

Date_____ Time_____

Exhausted · Overwhelm · Focused · Centered · High Vibin'

Today I found joy in the moment, like a pet's snuggle, or child's laughter. That moment today was...

Today's Positive Affirmation/Intention

Date_____ Time_____

Exhausted · Overwhelm · Focused · Centered · High Vibin'

Gratitude is the foundation for joy and today I am grateful for...

Today's Positive Affirmation/Intention

Date_____ Time_____

Exhausted · Overwhelm · Focused · Centered · High Vibin'

Comparison steals our joy. Where do I notice I compare myself to others and how does it make me feel?

Today's Positive Affirmation/Intention

Date_____ Time_____

Exhausted · Overwhelm · Focused · Centered · High Vibin'

What comparisons or expectations am I ready to let go of that are keeping me from living in more joy?

Today's Positive Affirmation/Intention

Date_____ Time_____

Exhausted · Overwhelm · Focused · Centered · High Vibin'

What am I grateful for today and how does it make me feel?

Today's Positive Affirmation/Intention

Date_____ Time_____

Exhausted · Overwhelm · Focused · Centered · High Vibin'

If I commit to a daily gratitude practice through this journaling experience, how might I celebrate? How will I feel?

Today's Positive Affirmation/Intention

Date_____ Time_____

Exhausted · Overwhelm · Focused · Centered · High Vibin'

Who is someone I am grateful for in this moment and why?

Today's Positive Affirmation/Intention

Date_____ Time_____

Exhausted · Overwhelm · Focused · Centered · High Vibin'

What experiences am I most grateful in this moment?

Today's Positive Affirmation/Intention

Date_____ Time_____

Exhausted · Overwhelm · Focused · Centered · High Vibin'

What does gratitude feel like in my body? Where do I notice it?

Today's Positive Affirmation/Intention

Date_____ Time_____

Exhausted · Overwhelm · Focused · Centered · High Vibin'

What is one quality about myself that I am grateful for in this moment?

Today's Positive Affirmation/Intention

Date_____ Time_____

Exhausted · Overwhelm · Focused · Centered · High Vibin'

What is a challenge that I might be willing to seek gratitude in (person, experience, inner critic)?

Today's Positive Affirmation/Intention

Date_____ Time_____

Exhausted · Overwhelm · Focused · Centered · High Vibin'

What am I grateful for today? What aligned action or small step am I willing to take to share this gratitude?

Today's Positive Affirmation/Intention

July

"If you are always trying to be normal you will never know
how amazing you can be."
—Maya Angelou

Date_____ Time_____

Exhausted · Overwhelm · Focused · Centered · High Vibin'

How will I make today an amazing experience for myself, my work, and my loved ones?daily practice of journaling?

Today's Positive Affirmation/Intention

Date_____ Time_____

Exhausted · Overwhelm · Focused · Centered · High Vibin'

How do I wish to feel as I go through the day today?daily practice of journaling?

Today's Positive Affirmation/Intention

Date_____ Time_____

Exhausted · Overwhelm · Focused · Centered · High Vibin'

My favorite moments of the day are when I...

Today's Positive Affirmation/Intention

Date_____ Time_____

Exhausted · Overwhelm · Focused · Centered · High Vibin'

Wow! I amaze myself when...

Today's Positive Affirmation/Intention

223

Date_____ Time_____

Exhausted · Overwhelm · Focused · Centered · High Vibin'

My most memorable moment this past week was... and it made me
feel... I will remember it because...

Today's Positive Affirmation/Intention

Date_____ Time_____

Exhausted · Overwhelm · Focused · Centered · High Vibin'

I am so grateful for everything I already have. What I currently do not have but want to call into my life and am ready to receive is...

Today's Positive Affirmation/Intention

Date_____ Time_____

Exhausted · Overwhelm · Focused · Centered · High Vibin'

Showing up each day and being the person that I desire to identify with most allows or will allow me to...

Today's Positive Affirmation/Intention

Date_____ Time_____

Exhausted · Overwhelm · Focused · Centered · High Vibin'

Today I give myself permission to rest and restore. It will look like...
That makes me feel...

Today's Positive Affirmation/Intention

Date_____ Time_____

Exhausted · Overwhelm · Focused · Centered · High Vibin'

A new habit I would like to create in my life and I am grateful for the awareness around is... I will begin by...

Today's Positive Affirmation/Intention

Date_____ Time_____

Exhausted · Overwhelm · Focused · Centered · High Vibin'

My new self talk around this new habit I intend to create today sounds like...

Today's Positive Affirmation/Intention

Date_____ Time_____

Exhausted · Overwhelm · Focused · Centered · High Vibin'

Today I get to be someone who...

Today's Positive Affirmation/Intention

Date_____ Time_____

Exhausted · Overwhelm · Focused · Centered · High Vibin'

What can I acknowledge myself for in this moment around journaling?
Journaling has allowed me to...

Today's Positive Affirmation/Intention

Date_____ Time_____

Exhausted · Overwhelm · Focused · Centered · High Vibin'

What am I looking forward to this month? How do I feel about it?
What about it am I looking forward to the most?

Today's Positive Affirmation/Intention

Date_____ Time_____

Exhausted · Overwhelm · Focused · Centered · High Vibin'

What are some of my unique gifts and talents? Make a list of all of them. The top 5 of these gifts and talents I am most proud of are...

Today's Positive Affirmation/Intention

Date_____ Time_____

Exhausted · Overwhelm · Focused · Centered · High Vibin'

Today I am going to ask 5 friends and loved ones what 5 qualities they see in me and I will write them here. The top 5 qualities and character-istic I see in myself are... The 5 that I loved hearing reflected back to me from my loved ones are... What did I love about this refection?

Today's Positive Affirmation/Intention

Date_____ Time_____

Exhausted · Overwhelm · Focused · Centered · High Vibin'

Today I am going to list all of the personality and characteristic traits that are unique to me and why they are unique to me.

Today's Positive Affirmation/Intention

Date_____ Time_____

Exhausted · Overwhelm · Focused · Centered · High Vibin'

Today I am reflecting on the challenges in my life that are unique to my life experiences. What did I overcome? What did I learn from these experiences? How have I grown? What can I be grateful for when I think about how I have grown?

Today's Positive Affirmation/Intention

Date_____ Time_____

Exhausted · Overwhelm · Focused · Centered · High Vibin'

I have skills that are so easy for me that I often forget to share with others. Today I am going to make a list of all the unique skills that I have learned. Then I will highlight the top 5 I enjoy the most and they are...

Today's Positive Affirmation/Intention

Date_____ Time_____

Exhausted · Overwhelm · Focused · Centered · High Vibin'

What are things that I am already doing that I enjoy doing and come easily and naturally for me?

Today's Positive Affirmation/Intention

Date_____ Time_____

Exhausted · Overwhelm · Focused · Centered · High Vibin'

What makes me unique when I look at the things I love? My skills?
Gifts? Experiences? Challenges? Talents? Qualities? What make me,
me?

Today's Positive Affirmation/Intention

Date_____ Time_____

Exhausted · Overwhelm · Focused · Centered · High Vibin'

What motivates me or who inspires me in my life? Why?

Today's Positive Affirmation/Intention

Date_____ Time_____

Exhausted · Overwhelm · Focused · Centered · High Vibin'

What tools have I learned (i.e. enneagram, Human Design, Myers Briggs, Gallop, etc.) that help me understand why I am the way I am? What did I learn from them?

Today's Positive Affirmation/Intention

Date_____ Time_____

Exhausted · Overwhelm · Focused · Centered · High Vibin'

What characteristics or gifts am I ready to step into that bring me joy and light me up?

Today's Positive Affirmation/Intention

Date_____ Time_____

Exhausted · Overwhelm · Focused · Centered · High Vibin'

What fears and doubts do I have around stepping into the gifts and talents that bring me joy?

Today's Positive Affirmation/Intention

Date_____ Time_____

Exhausted · Overwhelm · Focused · Centered · High Vibin'

What people, places, or things bring me joy and why?

Today's Positive Affirmation/Intention

Date_____ Time_____

Exhausted · Overwhelm · Focused · Centered · High Vibin'

What story do I notice when it comes to me living my purpose and enjoying it?

Today's Positive Affirmation/Intention

Date_____ Time_____

Exhausted · Overwhelm · Focused · Centered · High Vibin'

What does it mean for me to show up authentically?

Today's Positive Affirmation/Intention

Date_____ Time_____

Exhausted · Overwhelm · Focused · Centered · High Vibin'

What does it mean for me to live and speak my truth? How do others respond, and what does it say about me?

Today's Positive Affirmation/Intention

Date_____ Time_____

Exhausted · Overwhelm · Focused · Centered · High Vibin'

Where are the areas in life where I am not living or speaking my truth, or showing up authentically, and how does it make me feel?

Today's Positive Affirmation/Intention

Date_____ Time_____

Exhausted · Overwhelm · Focused · Centered · High Vibin'

Change begins with small actions. What is one area of my life I am willing to show up more authentically and in my truth? Why does this matter to me?

Today's Positive Affirmation/Intention

Date_____ Time_____

Exhausted · Overwhelm · Focused · Centered · High Vibin'

What have I learned about myself around how I feel about living my truth, being authentic, and speaking my truth?

Today's Positive Affirmation/Intention

August

"In order to carry a positive action
we must develop here a positive vision"
—Dalai Lama

Date_____ Time_____

Exhausted · Overwhelm · Focused · Centered · High Vibin'

What can I acknowledge myself for in this moment?

Today's Positive Affirmation/Intention

Date_____ Time_____

Exhausted · Overwhelm · Focused · Centered · High Vibin'

What am I looking forward to this month? How do I feel about it?
What about it am I looking forward to?

Today's Positive Affirmation/Intention

Date_____ Time_____

Exhausted · Overwhelm · Focused · Centered · High Vibin'

What is my relationship to my energy levels to do the things I want to in life?

Today's Positive Affirmation/Intention

Date_____ Time_____

Exhausted · Overwhelm · Focused · Centered · High Vibin'

What have I learned about energy? What are my beliefs about it?
Where does it show up?

Today's Positive Affirmation/Intention

Date_____ Time_____

Exhausted · Overwhelm · Focused · Centered · High Vibin'

What relationship do I have with trust?

Today's Positive Affirmation/Intention

Date_____ Time_____

Exhausted · Overwhelm · Focused · Centered · High Vibin'

What do I know about my intuition? Do I notice it? How does it show up? If I don't, are there resources for me to learn how to trust my intuition?

Today's Positive Affirmation/Intention

Date_____ Time_____

Exhausted · Overwhelm · Focused · Centered · High Vibin'

What does it mean to be aligned? What does alignment mean to me? What happens when things feel aligned and when they don't?

Today's Positive Affirmation/Intention

Date_____ Time_____

Exhausted · Overwhelm · Focused · Centered · High Vibin'

What would it look like to let go of hustle and step into alignment? How would my energy levels change?

Today's Positive Affirmation/Intention

Date_____ Time_____

Exhausted · Overwhelm · Focused · Centered · High Vibin'

What do I need to release to trust so I can let go of the hustle and live in alignment with my truth?

Today's Positive Affirmation/Intention

Date_____ Time_____

Exhausted · Overwhelm · Focused · Centered · High Vibin'

What does it say about me if I let go of the hustle, overwhelm, perfections, and over-giving?

Today's Positive Affirmation/Intention

Date_____ Time_____

Exhausted · Overwhelm · Focused · Centered · High Vibin'

How do I feel in relation to human being vs. a human doing? Do I practice being, or am I caught up in too much doing?

Today's Positive Affirmation/Intention

Date_____ Time_____

Exhausted · Overwhelm · Focused · Centered · High Vibin'

I know my worth is in my being and it shows up in these ways... If I step into this, who do I become?

Today's Positive Affirmation/Intention

Date_____ Time_____

Exhausted · Overwhelm · Focused · Centered · High Vibin'

These are the physical things I do that I am really good at... and it says this about me... If I let go of these who do I become?

Today's Positive Affirmation/Intention

Date_____ Time_____

Exhausted · Overwhelm · Focused · Centered · High Vibin'

What is the story around my worth when it comes to trying to prove myself?

Today's Positive Affirmation/Intention

Date_____ Time_____

Exhausted · Overwhelm · Focused · Centered · High Vibin'

What areas of my life do I find myself constantly proving my worth? When I think about proving myself, whose validation am I seeking and why? How does it make me feel? How is it impacting my life?

Today's Positive Affirmation/Intention

Date_____ Time_____

Exhausted · Overwhelm · Focused · Centered · High Vibin'

What is the underlying need in the ways in which I feel I have to prove my worth? How does it make me feel and what do I really need?

Today's Positive Affirmation/Intention

Date_____ Time_____

Exhausted · Overwhelm · Focused · Centered · High Vibin'

When I think of the needs to feel worthy, loved, safe, valuable, and lovable, I notice that the one that shows up for me the most is... The first time I remember feeling this way was at the age of... The story I have created around this is...

Today's Positive Affirmation/Intention

Date_____ Time_____

Exhausted · Overwhelm · Focused · Centered · High Vibin'

My need is to feel (i.e. safe, loved, lovable, hopeful, seen, heard, validated, appreciated, or some other)... How is this impacting relationships in my life? My health?

Today's Positive Affirmation/Intention

Date_____ Time_____

Exhausted · Overwhelm · Focused · Centered · High Vibin'

My need is to feel... How is this impacting relationships in my life? My job or career?

Today's Positive Affirmation/Intention

Date_____ Time_____

Exhausted · Overwhelm · Focused · Centered · High Vibin'

My need is to feel... How is this impacting relationships in my life around my happiness?

Today's Positive Affirmation/Intention

Date_____ Time_____

Exhausted · Overwhelm · Focused · Centered · High Vibin'

My need is to feel... How is this impacting relationships in my life around living in my purpose?

Today's Positive Affirmation/Intention

Date_____ Time_____

Exhausted · Overwhelm · Focused · Centered · High Vibin'

What is one way I am not fulling living up to my potential? How does this make me feel?

Today's Positive Affirmation/Intention

Date_____ Time_____

Exhausted · Overwhelm · Focused · Centered · High Vibin'

What is one area of my life I would like to improve?

Today's Positive Affirmation/Intention

Date_____ Time_____

Exhausted · Overwhelm · Focused · Centered · High Vibin'

What is one quality or characteristic I would like to change and why?

Today's Positive Affirmation/Intention

Date_____ Time_____

Exhausted · Overwhelm · Focused · Centered · High Vibin'

What is one quality or characteristic that I know is not perfect and I am willing to embrace? How does this make me feel? How will I practice embracing this? What are the ways in which I show up perfectly imperfect and I am willing to accept gracefully?

Today's Positive Affirmation/Intention

Date_____ Time_____

Exhausted · Overwhelm · Focused · Centered · High Vibin'

How will people respond when I speak my truth and show up in my authenticity?

Today's Positive Affirmation/Intention

Date_____ Time_____

Exhausted · Overwhelm · Focused · Centered · High Vibin'

What are the ways I exhaust myself trying to create change when maybe it's an invitation for acceptance?

Today's Positive Affirmation/Intention

Date_____ Time_____

Exhausted · Overwhelm · Focused · Centered · High Vibin'

Who do I know that loves me just the way I am and will support me to continue living authentically and aligned with my truth? If I struggle with this, can I count on myself, God, or believe in something bigger than me to support me?

Today's Positive Affirmation/Intention

Date_____ Time_____

Why is it important for me to begin living more aligned with my personal truth and showing up authentically now?

Today's Positive Affirmation/Intention

Date_____ Time_____

Exhausted · Overwhelm · Focused · Centered · High Vibin'

What have learned about myself around my authenticity and living my truth?

Today's Positive Affirmation/Intention

Date_____ Time_____

Exhausted · Overwhelm · Focused · Centered · High Vibin'

Today's Positive Affirmation/Intention

September

"Our deepest fear is not that we are inadequate. Our deepest fear is that we are powerful beyond measure. It is our light, not our darkness that most frightens us. We ask ourselves, 'Who am I to be brilliant, gorgeous, talented, fabulous?' Actually, who are you not to be? You are a child of God. Your playing small does not serve the world. There is nothing enlightened about shrinking so that other people won't feel insecure around you. We are all meant to shine, as children do. We were born to make manifest the glory of God that is within us. It's not just in some of us; it's in everyone. And as we let our own light shine, we unconsciously give other people permission to do the same. As we are liberated from our own fear, our presence automatically liberates others."
—Marianne Wiliamson

Date_____ Time_____

Exhausted · Overwhelm · Focused · Centered · High Vibin'

What would my life look like if committed to a small practice of a morning routine every day for 30 days? What might I be willing to try out for 30 days in addition to this journaling?

Today's Positive Affirmation/Intention

Date_____ Time_____

Exhausted · Overwhelm · Focused · Centered · High Vibin'

How does a morning routine impact my life in other areas of life?

Today's Positive Affirmation/Intention

Date_____ Time_____

Exhausted · Overwhelm · Focused · Centered · High Vibin'

How do I show up when I fall off the positive routines and healthy habits that I want to integrate into my life?

Today's Positive Affirmation/Intention

Date_____ Time_____

Exhausted · Overwhelm · Focused · Centered · High Vibin'

What kind of person do I want to be when I notice I fall out of my habits?

Today's Positive Affirmation/Intention

Date_____ Time_____

Exhausted · Overwhelm · Focused · Centered · High Vibin'

How do I feel when I have created new healthy habits and routines in my life?

Today's Positive Affirmation/Intention

Date_____ Time_____

Exhausted · Overwhelm · Focused · Centered · High Vibin'

What do I believe is standing in the way of me creating a consistent morning routine?

Today's Positive Affirmation/Intention

Date_____ Time_____

Exhausted · Overwhelm · Focused · Centered · High Vibin'

What can I tell myself or do when I notice I am falling off track so that I jump right back on?

Today's Positive Affirmation/Intention

Date_____ Time_____

Exhausted · Overwhelm · Focused · Centered · High Vibin'

What does the phrase "anything or everything is possible" mean to me?

Today's Positive Affirmation/Intention

Date_____ Time_____

Exhausted · Overwhelm · Focused · Centered · High Vibin'

What areas of my life do I notice are overbooked and make me feel overwhelmed? How can I simply my life when I notice these areas?

Today's Positive Affirmation/Intention

Date_____ Time_____

Exhausted · Overwhelm · Focused · Centered · High Vibin'

Simplifying my life in one small way will allow me to be more intentional with my time and create a small practice every day that keeps me aligned. When I think about this I feel... and I am willing to... for the next 30 days.

Today's Positive Affirmation/Intention

Date_____ Time_____

Exhausted · Overwhelm · Focused · Centered · High Vibin'

What are two distractions I can minimize to commit to my morning routine?

Today's Positive Affirmation/Intention

Date_____ Time_____

Exhausted · Overwhelm · Focused · Centered · High Vibin'

My morning routine starts with bedtime. How do I feel about my current bedtime routine and quality of sleep?

Today's Positive Affirmation/Intention

295

Date_____ Time_____

Exhausted · Overwhelm · Focused · Centered · High Vibin'

What are two distractions I can minimize to commit to my evening routine?

Today's Positive Affirmation/Intention

Date_____ Time_____

Exhausted · Overwhelm · Focused · Centered · High Vibin'

What would an ideal and realistic morning routine be for me (i.e. breathwork, yoga, movement, stretching, meditation, drinking water, prayer, walking)?

Today's Positive Affirmation/Intention

Date_____ Time_____

Exhausted · Overwhelm · Focused · Centered · High Vibin'

What is one moment today where I want to be more present and less distracted?

Today's Positive Affirmation/Intention

Date_____ Time_____

Exhausted · Overwhelm · Focused · Centered · High Vibin'

Who is someone in my life I want to be more present with and spend more time with and why?

Today's Positive Affirmation/Intention

Date_____ Time_____

Exhausted · Overwhelm · Focused · Centered · High Vibin'

Who is someone in my life who drains my energy and why? What about them drains me?

Today's Positive Affirmation/Intention

Date_____ Time_____

Exhausted · Overwhelm · Focused · Centered · High Vibin'

Thinking about this energy drain, what do I notice about how I feel? Is this a healthy and balanced relationship?

Today's Positive Affirmation/Intention

Date_____ Time_____

Exhausted · Overwhelm · Focused · Centered · High Vibin'

What do I notice about the way I feel when I am with this person?

Today's Positive Affirmation/Intention

Date_____ Time_____

Exhausted · Overwhelm · Focused · Centered · High Vibin'

What do I notice about my current flow of life? Is it cyclical or structured? Do I want more structure or flow? What does this mean to me or say about me?

Today's Positive Affirmation/Intention

Date_____ Time_____

Exhausted · Overwhelm · Focused · Centered · High Vibin'

What current practice am I committed to around creating a small and intentional routine in my life?

Today's Positive Affirmation/Intention

Date_____ Time_____

Exhausted · Overwhelm · Focused · Centered · High Vibin'

How do I feel about a practice of journaling, reflection, prayer, and meditation? Am I currently doing this or do I want more? What emotions or thoughts come up?

Today's Positive Affirmation/Intention

Date_____ Time_____

Exhausted · Overwhelm · Focused · Centered · High Vibin'

What space do I like to create that gets me in the mood for a routine or ritual? How am I willing to implement this?

Today's Positive Affirmation/Intention

Date_____ Time_____

Exhausted · Overwhelm · Focused · Centered · High Vibin'

Today I am excited about... and this makes me feel...

Today's Positive Affirmation/Intention

Date_____ Time_____

Exhausted · Overwhelm · Focused · Centered · High Vibin'

Today I want to remember what I love in life. What lights me up is...

Today's Positive Affirmation/Intention

Date_____ Time_____

Exhausted · Overwhelm · Focused · Centered · High Vibin'

When I think about the things that light me up, here are the reasons...

Today's Positive Affirmation/Intention

Date_____ Time_____

Exhausted · Overwhelm · Focused · Centered · High Vibin'

When I think about the things that light me up, it makes me feel...

Today's Positive Affirmation/Intention

Date_____ Time_____

Exhausted · Overwhelm · Focused · Centered · High Vibin'

The people places or things reflected in these things that I love are...

Today's Positive Affirmation/Intention

Exhausted · Overwhelm · Focused · Centered · High Vibin'

If I saw an old friend from childhood today, what would they say or think about me?

Today's Positive Affirmation/Intention

Date_____ Time_____

Exhausted · Overwhelm · Focused · Centered · High Vibin'

What is one book I can revisit or buy new today that will help me invest time in myself?

Today's Positive Affirmation/Intention

October

"If you want to awaken all of humanity, then awaken all of yourself.
If you want to eliminate the suffering in the world,
then eliminate all that is dark and negative in yourself.
Truly, the greatest gift you have to give is that
of your own self-transformation."
—Lao Tzu

Date_____ Time_____

Exhausted · Overwhelm · Focused · Centered · High Vibin'

Who is one person that motivates or inspires me in my life and why?

Today's Positive Affirmation/Intention

Date_____ Time_____

Exhausted · Overwhelm · Focused · Centered · High Vibin'

When I think of this person, it makes me feel...

Today's Positive Affirmation/Intention

Date_____ Time_____

Exhausted · Overwhelm · Focused · Centered · High Vibin'

When I think of this person I see them as a reflection of me in theses ways . . .

Today's Positive Affirmation/Intention

Date_____ Time_____

Exhausted · Overwhelm · Focused · Centered · High Vibin'

When I think of this person, I feel different from them in that I...

Today's Positive Affirmation/Intention

Date_____ Time_____

Exhausted · Overwhelm · Focused · Centered · High Vibin'

When was the last time I made a decision out of alignment with my values and how did that turn out?

Today's Positive Affirmation/Intention

Date_____ Time_____

Exhausted · Overwhelm · Focused · Centered · High Vibin'

Where am I no longer choosing to compromise my values in life?

Today's Positive Affirmation/Intention

Date_____ Time_____

Exhausted · Overwhelm · Focused · Centered · High Vibin'

When was the last time I took action aligned with my values and how did that turn out?

Today's Positive Affirmation/Intention

Date_____ Time_____

Exhausted · Overwhelm · Focused · Centered · High Vibin'

What challenge am I ready to move past today and how do I feel about that?

Today's Positive Affirmation/Intention

Date_____ Time_____

Exhausted · Overwhelm · Focused · Centered · High Vibin'

If I were to stop making excuses in my life, how would I show up differently?

Today's Positive Affirmation/Intention

Date_____ Time_____

Exhausted · Overwhelm · Focused · Centered · High Vibin'

What is one unique thing about me that makes me special?

Today's Positive Affirmation/Intention

Date_____ Time_____

Exhausted · Overwhelm · Focused · Centered · High Vibin'

What are my gifts and talents?

Today's Positive Affirmation/Intention

Date_____ Time_____

Exhausted · Overwhelm · Focused · Centered · High Vibin'

What unique experiences have I had in life?

Today's Positive Affirmation/Intention

Date_____ Time_____

Exhausted · Overwhelm · Focused · Centered · High Vibin'

What do I stand for in this world? Why is this important to me?

Today's Positive Affirmation/Intention

Date_____ Time_____

Exhausted · Overwhelm · Focused · Centered · High Vibin'

What do I stand against in this world? Why is this important to me?

Today's Positive Affirmation/Intention

Date_____ Time_____

Exhausted · Overwhelm · Focused · Centered · High Vibin'

What do I know is my unwavering truth no matter what?

Today's Positive Affirmation/Intention

Date_____ Time_____

Exhausted · Overwhelm · Focused · Centered · High Vibin'

What does fear mean to me? Where does it currently show up in my life?

Today's Positive Affirmation/Intention

Date_____ Time_____

Exhausted · Overwhelm · Focused · Centered · High Vibin'

As I think about stepping out into the world as this new version of myself, what responses, fears, or beliefs come up?

Today's Positive Affirmation/Intention

Date_____ Time_____

Exhausted · Overwhelm · Focused · Centered · High Vibin'

What role has fear played in my life? What impact has it made? What is it keeping me from and how do I feel about it?

Today's Positive Affirmation/Intention

Date_____ Time_____

Exhausted · Overwhelm · Focused · Centered · High Vibin'

If I were to welcome my fear and remember a time I felt fear, what would I notice? What sensations come up? Where do I feel it in my body? Is there a temperature, color, shape, texture, size associated with it? What is the full experience?

Today's Positive Affirmation/Intention

Date_____ Time_____

Exhausted · Overwhelm · Focused · Centered · High Vibin'

If I dig deeper around my fear and allow myself to be present with it again, and ask myself "Why is this here to teach me? what can I lean into, observe, or witness as an outsider?"

Today's Positive Affirmation/Intention

Date_____ Time_____

Exhausted · Overwhelm · Focused · Centered · High Vibin'

Now that I have welcomed and observed our relationship to fear, I am ready to ask my body would what feel good to release or to express this fear. Is it movement? Anger burn? Play? What does my body want to do to release this fear?

Today's Positive Affirmation/Intention

Date_____ Time_____

Exhausted · Overwhelm · Focused · Centered · High Vibin'

I know vulnerability is the gateway to my potential. I am ready to transmute the fear into courage. Here are 5-10 things I am willing to explore at the depths of my fear that require courage...

Today's Positive Affirmation/Intention

Date_____ Time_____

Exhausted · Overwhelm · Focused · Centered · High Vibin'

What if I allowed that fear to ignite my gifts? What if I acted with courage through next steps? What might be possible for me? What new beliefs am I willing to create around fear and how am I willing to show up moving forward?

Today's Positive Affirmation/Intention

Date_____ Time_____

Exhausted · Overwhelm · Focused · Centered · High Vibin'

I am going to celebrate myself for acknowledging my fears and the
willingness to move through them. I will do this by...

Today's Positive Affirmation/Intention

Exhausted · Overwhelm · Focused · Centered · High Vibin'

What have a learned around my relationship to fear? What is my biggest takeaway that I am most grateful for?

Today's Positive Affirmation/Intention

Date_____ Time_____

Exhausted · Overwhelm · Focused · Centered · High Vibin'

I am so grateful for the awareness of these fears that have now illuminated new possibilities for me. Here is what I have been shown is now
possible.

Today's Positive Affirmation/Intention

Date_____ Time_____

Exhausted · Overwhelm · Focused · Centered · High Vibin'

Showing up each day as the person I desire to identify with most without fear holding me back allows me to or will allow me to ...

Today's Positive Affirmation/Intention

Date_____ Time_____

Exhausted · Overwhelm · Focused · Centered · High Vibin'

Today I will reflect on all that I have leaned in to and learned. My self talk around fear is...

Today's Positive Affirmation/Intention

Date_____ Time_____

Exhausted · Overwhelm · Focused · Centered · High Vibin'

Today I get to be someone who... through my fears. When I think about how this is impacting my life through these new empowering choices, I feel... When I am feeling really brave, I might even be ready to...

Today's Positive Affirmation/Intention

Date_____ Time_____

Exhausted · Overwhelm · Focused · Centered · High Vibin'

When I look back at these past few weeks, I notice that journaling around fear has allowed me to...

Today's Positive Affirmation/Intention

Date_____ Time_____

Exhausted · Overwhelm · Focused · Centered · High Vibin'

If everything I desire is on the other side of my fear, what I am ready to welcome into my life?

Today's Positive Affirmation/Intention

November

"Never give up on a dream just because of the time will take to
accomplish it. The time will pass anyway"
—Earl Nightingale

Date_____ Time_____

Exhausted · Overwhelm · Focused · Centered · High Vibin'

Now that I have worked through some fear and am more open to receiving, I am ready to explore my relationship to abundance. What is abundance to me? How does it look? How does it feel?

Today's Positive Affirmation/Intention

Date_____ Time_____

Exhausted · Overwhelm · Focused · Centered · High Vibin'

What is my relationship to abundance? Where do I notice plenty or lack of abundance in my life?

Today's Positive Affirmation/Intention

Date_____ Time_____

Exhausted · Overwhelm · Focused · Centered · High Vibin'

What are my beliefs around abundance and scarcity or lack? With money? Relationships Health? The relationship I would like to heal around abundance is...

Today's Positive Affirmation/Intention

Date_____ Time_____

Exhausted · Overwhelm · Focused · Centered · High Vibin'

The area of my life where I would like more abundance is... When I have this, I will feel... and it will give me...

Today's Positive Affirmation/Intention

Date_____ Time_____

Exhausted · Overwhelm · Focused · Centered · High Vibin'

The areas of my life that I am wanting and willing to receive more in is...
When I do this, it will feel... and I will know because.... I am willing to
lean into receiving more. Support around this might look like...

Today's Positive Affirmation/Intention

Date_____ Time_____

Exhausted · Overwhelm · Focused · Centered · High Vibin'

I have been blocking my ability to receive abundance by... Where or who do I resist? If I become curious about what is underneath this, what do I notice?

Today's Positive Affirmation/Intention

Date_____ Time_____

Exhausted · Overwhelm · Focused · Centered · High Vibin'

Today I am going to reflect on my relationship with money. I am going to go on a date with money and tell him/her everything I feel. This is what I plan to say...

Today's Positive Affirmation/Intention

354

Date_____ Time_____

Exhausted · Overwhelm · Focused · Centered · High Vibin'

What does money mean to me? I believe money is...

Today's Positive Affirmation/Intention

Date_____ Time_____

Exhausted · Overwhelm · Focused · Centered · High Vibin'

My beliefs around earning or having money are... I believe that I have to... to earn money. I believe... around keeping money. I believe... around giving money. I believe... around receiving money.

Today's Positive Affirmation/Intention

356

Date_____ Time_____

Exhausted · Overwhelm · Focused · Centered · High Vibin'

Today I am willing to look at my financial situation. When I see this, I notice I feel... I am ready to reframe and embody this as a new empowering belief. My new reframe is... and it makes me feel...

Today's Positive Affirmation/Intention

Date_____ Time_____

Exhausted · Overwhelm · Focused · Centered · High Vibin'

The belief I am willing to change around money is... When I look at my current financial situation and the new belief I am choosing to embody, I feel...

Today's Positive Affirmation/Intention

Date_____ Time_____

Exhausted · Overwhelm · Focused · Centered · High Vibin'

When I reflect on my relationship with money, I notice blocks in the areas of earning/owning/receiving/trusting/keeping money... If I dive deeper, I also notice that these blocks might show up in other areas of my life such as...

Today's Positive Affirmation/Intention

Date_____ Time_____

Exhausted · Overwhelm · Focused · Centered · High Vibin'

I am creating new awareness on how my beliefs have impacted my current reality. Before I was aware of this I was... with money and it made me feel... Moving forward I am choosing my new reality around money and that looks like...

Today's Positive Affirmation/Intention

Date_____ Time_____

Exhausted · Overwhelm · Focused · Centered · High Vibin'

I am excited about the possibility of financial freedom and becoming curious about it. Financial freedom looks and feels like (amount of money work, feelings, time, support) ... When I step into financial freedom it will give me... My life will change by...

Today's Positive Affirmation/Intention

Date_____ Time_____

Exhausted · Overwhelm · Focused · Centered · High Vibin'

Now that I know that financial freedom looks and feels like, I am excited to welcome and celebrate financial freedom in my life . These are the ways in which I plan to celebrate...

Today's Positive Affirmation/Intention

Exhausted · Overwhelm · Focused · Centered · High Vibin'

I am willing to become curious around financial freedom, intimacy, and receiving. Today I am going to reflect on my relationship with love. I am going to go on a date with love and tell him/her everything I feel. This is what I plan to say...

Today's Positive Affirmation/Intention

Date_____ Time_____

Exhausted · Overwhelm · Focused · Centered · High Vibin'

I believe love is...

Today's Positive Affirmation/Intention

Date_____ Time_____

Exhausted · Overwhelm · Focused · Centered · High Vibin'

When I look at my relationship to love and intimacy I notice I am blocked in receiving/trusting/earning/keeping love in these areas of my life...

Today's Positive Affirmation/Intention

Date_____ Time_____

Exhausted · Overwhelm · Focused · Centered · High Vibin'

I have been blocking my ability to receive love by... Where do I resist?
With whom do I resist?

Today's Positive Affirmation/Intention

Date_____ Time_____

Exhausted · Overwhelm · Focused · Centered · High Vibin'

My beliefs about receiving, earning, having, or giving love are... I believe that I have to... to earn/receive/keep/give love.

Today's Positive Affirmation/Intention

Date_____ Time_____

Exhausted · Overwhelm · Focused · Centered · High Vibin'

Before I was aware of this belief, I was... with love. Being this way with love made me feel... Moving forward I am choosing...

Today's Positive Affirmation/Intention

Date_____ Time_____

Exhausted · Overwhelm · Focused · Centered · High Vibin'

Freedom around my relationship with love looks and feels like... I will
choose to believe... about love and will celebrate this new belief by...

Today's Positive Affirmation/Intention

Date_____ Time_____

Exhausted · Overwhelm · Focused · Centered · High Vibin'

Today I am reflecting on my relationship with health and well-being (well-th is abundance including health). I am going to go on a date with health and tell him/her everything I feel. This is what I plan to say...

Today's Positive Affirmation/Intention

Date_____ Time_____

Exhausted · Overwhelm · Focused · Centered · High Vibin'

I believe health is...

Today's Positive Affirmation/Intention

Date_____ Time_____

Exhausted · Overwhelm · Focused · Centered · High Vibin'

Today I am willing to look at my true current health situation. If I look deeply I notice and feel... around my health. I am ready to shift my relationship to my health and well-being by...

Today's Positive Affirmation/Intention

Date_____ Time_____

Exhausted · Overwhelm · Focused · Centered · High Vibin'

I am curious about the ways in which I block my ability to receive and live in health and well-being. This shows up in these three areas of my life... What patterns do I notice?

Today's Positive Affirmation/Intention

Date_____ Time_____

Exhausted · Overwhelm · Focused · Centered · High Vibin'

I am able to see unhealthy fears, blocks, and patterns around my relationship with my well-being. These include... I am willing to transmute these fears, blocks, and patterns by taking small aligned actions to create change. One small action step I am willing to take today is...

Today's Positive Affirmation/Intention

Date_____ Time_____

Exhausted · Overwhelm · Focused · Centered · High Vibin'

When it comes to my health and well-being I am confident that I can...
and I am committed to...

Today's Positive Affirmation/Intention

Exhausted · Overwhelm · Focused · Centered · High Vibin'

Health freedom looks and feels like... From now on I will practice
health freedom by choosing...

Today's Positive Affirmation/Intention

Date_____ Time_____

Exhausted · Overwhelm · Focused · Centered · High Vibin'

I am willing to forgive myself for the people, places, things, and decisions where I was unhealthy with money, health, and love. Here are 10-15 things I am ready to forgive and release. The lesson I learned in all of this is...

Today's Positive Affirmation/Intention

December

"Change is not only inevitable, but always happening.
When you truly embrace this concept of
change being constant, the only thing left to do
is grow, detach, venture inwards, touch the spirit
and find your source — the one responsible for
keeping you grounded through the
ever-changing seasons of life."
—Julie Weiland

Date_____ Time_____

Exhausted · Overwhelm · Focused · Centered · High Vibin'

What is my vision or mission in life?

Today's Positive Affirmation/Intention

Date_____ Time_____

Exhausted · Overwhelm · Focused · Centered · High Vibin'

What makes me unique? List all the qualities, experiences, and characteristics here.

Today's Positive Affirmation/Intention

Date_____ Time_____

Exhausted · Overwhelm · Focused · Centered · High Vibin'

How do I serve or share my gifts? What comes naturally to me? What do people see in me?

Today's Positive Affirmation/Intention

Date_____ Time_____

Exhausted · Overwhelm · Focused · Centered · High Vibin'

I am willing to get creative and think of the potential global impact that my dreams and my presence alone can create. What is my big dream?

Today's Positive Affirmation/Intention

Date_____ Time_____

Exhausted · Overwhelm · Focused · Centered · High Vibin'

When I think about my dreams, why do they matter? Who will this impact?

Today's Positive Affirmation/Intention

384

Date_____ Time_____

Exhausted · Overwhelm · Focused · Centered · High Vibin'

What is stopping me from living my dream life?

Today's Positive Affirmation/Intention

Date_____ Time_____

Exhausted · Overwhelm · Focused · Centered · High Vibin'

What am I actually afraid of when it comes to claiming my dream life?

Today's Positive Affirmation/Intention

Date_____ Time_____

Exhausted · Overwhelm · Focused · Centered · High Vibin'

What is success to me? What does it mean? What does it say about me? Who did I learn this from?

Today's Positive Affirmation/Intention

Date_____ Time_____

Exhausted · Overwhelm · Focused · Centered · High Vibin'

If I had a magic wand, what 3 things would I change in my life right now?

Today's Positive Affirmation/Intention

Date_____ Time_____

Exhausted · Overwhelm · Focused · Centered · High Vibin'

What have I tried before to make changes in my life that worked? What have I tried that didn't work? How do I feel about these experiences?

Today's Positive Affirmation/Intention

Date_____ Time_____

Exhausted · Overwhelm · Focused · Centered · High Vibin'

What does it say about me if I achieve my dreams? What does it say about me if I don't?

Today's Positive Affirmation/Intention

Date_____ Time_____

Exhausted · Overwhelm · Focused · Centered · High Vibin'

Who are the people who will be there supporting me when I am achieving my goals and dreams? How will they respond? What will it look like?

Today's Positive Affirmation/Intention

Date_____ Time_____

Exhausted · Overwhelm · Focused · Centered · High Vibin'

What does my best self look and feel like?

Today's Positive Affirmation/Intention

Date_____ Time_____

Exhausted · Overwhelm · Focused · Centered · High Vibin'

What are 5 adjectives that best describe me?

Today's Positive Affirmation/Intention

Date_____ Time_____

Exhausted · Overwhelm · Focused · Centered · High Vibin'

What are my top 5 core values? What does each value mean to me specifically?

Today's Positive Affirmation/Intention

394

Date_____ Time_____

Exhausted · Overwhelm · Focused · Centered · High Vibin'

In what area of my life do I want to create change and how ready am I to create that change?

Today's Positive Affirmation/Intention

Date_____ Time_____

Exhausted · Overwhelm · Focused · Centered · High Vibin'

What happens when I feel ready to create change?

Today's Positive Affirmation/Intention

Date_____ Time_____

Exhausted · Overwhelm · Focused · Centered · High Vibin'

What happens when I am ready to receive support?

Today's Positive Affirmation/Intention

Date_____ Time_____

Exhausted · Overwhelm · Focused · Centered · High Vibin'

What happens when I am ready to act on my goals and dreams?

Today's Positive Affirmation/Intention

Date_____ Time_____

Exhausted · Overwhelm · Focused · Centered · High Vibin'

What fears do I have around living my dreams? What is an empowering way to reframe the fear?

Today's Positive Affirmation/Intention

Date_____ Time_____

Exhausted · Overwhelm · Focused · Centered · High Vibin'

What is my sabotaging core wound? Who do I need to forgive? What am I ready to release and reframe around my goals and dreams?

Today's Positive Affirmation/Intention

Date_____ Time_____

Exhausted · Overwhelm · Focused · Centered · High Vibin'

What are my survivor strategies? How have the served me? How and when do they show up?

Today's Positive Affirmation/Intention

Date_____ Time_____

Exhausted · Overwhelm · Focused · Centered · High Vibin'

What have I learned about myself? What is my potentially sabotaging behavior pattern that shows up? What happens after? How do I feel? What do I need? What am I willing to do about this?

Today's Positive Affirmation/Intention

Date_____ Time_____

Exhausted · Overwhelm · Focused · Centered · High Vibin'

What am I willing to acknowledge myself for around what I have learned about myself?

Today's Positive Affirmation/Intention

Date_____ Time_____

Exhausted · Overwhelm · Focused · Centered · High Vibin'

What am I willing to release around these stories, patterns, and beliefs
that are keeping me from living the life I want?

Today's Positive Affirmation/Intention

Date_____ Time_____

Exhausted · Overwhelm · Focused · Centered · High Vibin'

What is the story around what happens when I let go, release, or am no longer trapped in this story?

Today's Positive Affirmation/Intention

Date_____ Time_____

Exhausted · Overwhelm · Focused · Centered · High Vibin'

How is this new version of myself impacting the relationships in my life? With loved ones? With my health? With money?

Today's Positive Affirmation/Intention

Date_____ Time_____

Exhausted · Overwhelm · Focused · Centered · High Vibin'

What gifts can I bring forth to the world?

Today's Positive Affirmation/Intention

Date_____ Time_____

Exhausted · Overwhelm · Focused · Centered · High Vibin'

What do I stand for in the world? What do I stand against?

Today's Positive Affirmation/Intention

Date_____ Time_____

Exhausted · Overwhelm · Focused · Centered · High Vibin'

Today I am writing my legacy, my mission, my self devotion statement. I am clear on what I love in life, what I stand for, my values, and the impact I want to leave in the world. I am ready to claim it here in writing down my vision and promise to myself and the world around me.

Today's Positive Affirmation/Intention

Date_____ Time_____

Exhausted · Overwhelm · Focused · Centered · High Vibin'

Today I am writing a letter to myself and reviewing the year. I am sharing all of the celebrations, challenges, and events month by month. I will read this letter at the end of next year.

Today's Positive Affirmation/Intention

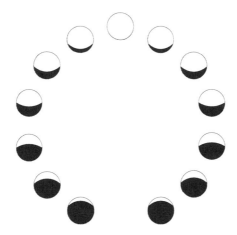

Phase III: New Moon Planning

How to Use this Section

Set Monthly New Moon Intentions:

1. Set Intention/Ritual: Create Sacred Space and time in your calendar for this each month. This is not a "to do" task; this is "you get to choose." Maybe you have a favorite journaling reflection space or routine. A favorite chair or meditation space. You may choose to light a candle, take a bath, listen to calming music.

2. Prayer Request. Say out loud: "Is there anything or any area of my life that needs healing or love? What am I ready to release and what am I willing to welcome in? What might be possible with this new intention?"

3. Energy Alignment: What do I want to do and how do I want to FEEL?

For more information join our membership for guidance and support each New Moon

Monthly New Moon Planning

Date:_____ Month_____

Astrological Sign_____ Theme:_____

1. Intention: Create the Space

2. Request: Reflections and Healing—What did I learn, how did I grow?

3. Alignment: What do I want to feel and experience?

Monthly New Moon Planning

Date:_____ Month_____

Astrological Sign_____ Theme:_____

1. Intention: Create the Space

2. Request: Reflections and Healing—What did I learn, how did I grow?

3. Alignment: What do I want to feel and experience?

Monthly New Moon Planning

Date:_____ Month_____

Astrological Sign_____ Theme:_____

1. Intention: Create the Space

2. Request: Reflections and Healing—What did I learn, how did I grow?

3. Alignment: What do I want to feel and experience?

Monthly New Moon Planning

Date:_____ Month_____

Astrological Sign_____ Theme:_____

1. Intention: Create the Space

2. Request: Reflections and Healing—What did I learn, how did I grow?

3. Alignment: What do I want to feel and experience?

Monthly New Moon Planning

Date:_____ Month_____

Astrological Sign_____ Theme:_____

1. Intention: Create the Space

2. Request: Reflections and Healing—What did I learn, how did I grow?

3. Alignment: What do I want to feel and experience?

Monthly New Moon Planning

Date:_____ Month_____

Astrological Sign_____ Theme:_____

1. Intention: Create the Space

2. Request: Reflections and Healing—What did I learn, how did I grow?

3. Alignment: What do I want to feel and experience?

Monthly New Moon Planning

Date:_____ Month_____

Astrological Sign_____ Theme:_____

1. Intention: Create the Space

2. Request: Reflections and Healing—What did I learn, how did I grow?

3. Alignment: What do I want to feel and experience?

Monthly New Moon Planning

Date:_____ Month_____

Astrological Sign_____ Theme:_____

1. Intention: Create the Space

2. Request: Reflections and Healing—What did I learn, how did I grow?

3. Alignment: What do I want to feel and experience?

Monthly New Moon Planning

Date:_____ Month_____

Astrological Sign_____   Theme:_____

1. Intention: Create the Space

2. Request: Reflections and Healing—What did I learn, how did I grow?

3. Alignment: What do I want to feel and experience?

Monthly New Moon Planning

Date:_____ Month_____

Astrological Sign_____ Theme:_____

1. Intention: Create the Space

2. Request: Reflections and Healing—What did I learn, how did I grow?

3. Alignment: What do I want to feel and experience?

Monthly New Moon Planning

Date:_____ Month_____

Astrological Sign_____ Theme:_____

1. Intention: Create the Space

2. Request: Reflections and Healing—What did I learn, how did I grow?

3. Alignment: What do I want to feel and experience?

Monthly New Moon Planning

Date:_____ Month_____

Astrological Sign_____ Theme:_____

1. Intention: Create the Space

2. Request: Reflections and Healing—What did I learn, how did I grow?

3. Alignment: What do I want to feel and experience?

Monthly New Moon Planning

Date:_____ Month_____

Astrological Sign_____   Theme:_____

1. Intention: Create the Space

2. Request: Reflections and Healing—What did I learn, how did I grow?

3. Alignment: What do I want to feel and experience?

Phase IV: Seasonal Planning

How to Use this Section:

1. Create 1-3 Goals for each of the 4 Seasons in the beginning of the year.

2. Schedule time in your calendar for 4 Seasonal Planning days.

3. On each Equinox or Solstice or within 7 days of them, revisit and realign your goals based on your monthly new moon reflections and intentions. The Equinox occurs on or around the 21st of the month in March, June, September, and December.

4. Join the Seasonal Planning workshops for additional guidance and support through our membership in the reproduce area.

Spring Equinox Cycle

Spring is the time to plant new seeds, plan projects, emerge, try something new, cleanse your energy of clutter (body, home, relationships)

Reflection/Growth/Gratitude:
Looking back over the past season, what themes do I notice? What did I learn? How did I grow?

What did I say yes to? What did I accomplish? What can I celebrate?

What worked and what didn't work for me when it came to my monthly intentions?

Goals/Planning

Applying what I learned from last season, and looking forward to what I want to step into, what goals do I have in each area of my well-being?

Why/Aligned Action

Looking at my goals, why do these matter? Based on my why, what aligned action am I willing to take in each of these areas to live with intention that is aligned to my planning goals?

Mental

Emotional

Physical

Spiritual

Financial

Summer Solstice Cycle

Summer is the time to connect, be social, get out in the community, become visible, travel. It's a time of longer and brighter days from the sun, and of optimized energy. This is your time for adventure and connection. A time for expansion.

Reflection/Growth/Gratitude:
Looking back over the past season, what themes do I notice? What did I learn? How did I grow?

What did I say yes to? What did I accomplish? What can I celebrate?

What worked and what didn't work for me when it came to my monthly intentions?

Goals/Planning

Applying what I learned from last season and looking forward, what do I want to step into? What goals do I have in each area of my well-being?

Why/Aligned Action

Looking at my goals, why do these matter? Based on my why, what aligned action am I willing to take in each of these areas to live with intention that is aligned to my planning goals?

Mental

Emotional

Physical

Spiritual

Financial

Fall Equinox Cycle

The Fall Season is an abundant time to gather, harvest, prepare for rest. A time of nesting, embodiment, gentle flow, movement, and connection to the body.

Reflection/Growth/Gratitude:

Looking back over the past season, what themes do I notice? What did I learn and how did I grow?

What did I say yes to? What did I accomplish? What can I celebrate?

What worked and what didn't work for me when it came to my monthly intentions?

Goals/Planning
Applying what I learned from last season and looking forward, what do I want to step into? What goals do I have in each area of my well-being?

Why/Aligned Action
Looking at my goals, why do these matter? Based on my why, what aligned action am I willing to take in each of these areas to live with intention that is aligned to my planning goals?

Mental

Emotional

Physical

Spiritual

Financial

Winter Solstice Cycle

Winter Season is a time for rest, rejuvenation, and hibernation. Nourish with nutrient-dense hearty foods. Reflect on the past year and prepare for the new calendar year with new intentions.

Reflection/Growth/Gratitude:

Looking back over the past season, what themes do I notice? What did I learn? How did I grow?

What did I say yes to? What did I accomplish? What can I celebrate?

What worked and what didn't work for me when it came to my monthly intentions?

Goals/Planning

Applying what I learned from last season and looking forward, what do I want to step into? What goals do I have in each area of my well-being?

Why/Aligned Action

Looking at my goals, why do these matter? Based on my why, what aligned action am I willing to take in each of these areas to live with intention that is aligned to my planning goals?

Mental

Emotional

Physical

Spiritual

Financial

Yearly Reflection

Take time to consider each monthly reflection, new moon planning, and the four seasons you wrote about. Think of this as writing a letter to yourself at the end of the year. You may even choose to write it as a letter and address it to yourself. Use the following questions as a guide for reflection.

Looking back over the year, what challenges did I overcome? What did I learn. How did I grow?

What happened over the year that I am ready to forgive myself and others for?

Is there anyone I need to apologize to?

Are there new boundaries I am ready to create?

What goals did I set that I did not reach? What areas need more attention in my life?

What am I choosing to be available for moving forward? What am I choosing to no longer be available for moving forward?

Looking back over the year and at my Celebrations, what were my top 10 achievements for the year?

What can I be thankful for, and how can I express gratitude to myself for this past year?

What relationships do I feel better about? (people, spouse, money, body, health, job)

What did I say no to? What did I say yes to?

What major events happened this year?

How did I give back to others?

What patterns or themes, if any, did I notice?

How do I feel about the changes I made?

What do I want to learn or explore, or new thing I want to try this coming year?

What new skills, talents, and activities do I want to learn in order to continue this path of personal growth and transformation?

How can I bring more harmony, ease, and grace into my life and relationships?

What habits, practices, and/or new beliefs will I take with me into next year? How do those fit into my big dream?

What am I willing to risk, invest, explore, or discover to walk the path towards my dream life?

To continue this journey and join our membership,
use code **dailydevotion22** to save 22% on 13 Moons Daily Devotion
Membership.

Please share this code with friends!

Gratitude List

"To express gratitude is gracious and honorable, to enact gratitude is generous and noble, but to live with gratitude ever in our hearts is to touch heaven."
— Thomas S. Monson

Use this area to keep track of your gratitude practice. You can copy from your daily journaling or jot down extra ones here.

The gift that keeps on giving, gratitude is a practice that can change the way you feel about yourself and your life. The practice and intention of finding gratitude in your daily life will encourage more joy, peace, and fulfillment. You can use this page daily or weekly to reflect and record what you are grateful for to help keep a positive mindset, or fill it as you feel compelled. Either way, I encourage you to occasionally read through all of the gratitudes that you have listed throughout the year. The practice of gratitude encourages self-awareness and healthy mental and emotional well-being. Practicing gratitude daily will gradually shift your perception of the world around you. You will notice that you find more to be grateful for, and you will find yourself choosing to be more grateful. Studies have shown that gratitude stimulates the hypothalamus to regulate stress as well as parts of the midbrain which produces feelings of pleasure through an increase of dopamine.

I encourage you to work up to a daily gratitude practice. You have a space in your journal each day. As you intentionally write down what you are grateful for on that day, sit with how it makes you feel. Allow the gratitude that is within you to anchor into your body. When we do this we begin to realize that we are gratitude. If we can feel gratitude for things outside of us and the feeling is created within, then we are gratitude. This embodiment of gratitude will begin to restructure your mindset and energetic imprint for what you are attracting to you in your life. Your energy and intention will flow more towards joy, appreciation, and fulfillment.

Gratitude List

Gratitude List

Gratitude List

Gratitude List

Celebrations

"There are only two ways to live your life. One is as though nothing is a miracle. The other is as though everything is a miracle."
—Albert Einstein

How often do you celebrate yourself, your accomplishments, your resiliency, the struggles you have had to overcome? As a lifelong coach, leader, and teacher, I have noticed that many of us forget to celebrate how far we have come. Sometimes it may feel easier to look at what isn't going well versus what is going well, and feel that life happens *to* us, not *for* us.

This celebration list is about you celebrating you. Standing up for yourself, speaking your truth, traveling to a new place, trying a new food, a new exercise routine, new friends, new relationships. Ask yourself, "What can I celebrate myself for today?" Take a moment at the end of each day, week, month, or after your new moon ceremony to write some celebrations down. Remember to spend time coming back to these pages, especially during challenging times. Celebrate the wins, the blessons (blessings from the lessons), the growth, the challenges you overcame. Nothing is too small to celebrate.

As a bonus let's create a reward for you celebrating yourself here. Is there someone you would like to share your celebrations with? Maybe it's just one or two or maybe the entire list. Do you have a spouse, friend, or accountability partner who would love to celebrate with you? Some of us struggle with being seen or heard in our celebrations. If this is you, I encourage you to share the celebrations and the struggles with loved ones. If that feels too big for now, start with the journal and see how it feels when you get to 10, then 25 celebrations. Or maybe you want to set a personal reward. You can start with setting an intention here to stay on track and commit to your celebrations.

When I reach 10 celebrations I will

_____

When I reach 25 celebrations I will

_____

When I reach 50 celebrations I will

_____

When I reach 100 celebrations I will

_____

Celebrations

Celebrations

Celebrations

Celebrations

Dream List

I have coached thousands of women to health, love, purpose, and financial freedom and am always surprised by the number of women who haven't taken the time to envision their big dream. Oftentimes we hold the role of mother, caregiver, nurturer, and even breadwinner but don't consider our own role of just being ourselves. We put everyone else's needs before our own and get lost in the identity of who we have become for everyone else. Somewhere along the way we lose the magic, imagination, wonder, and creative spirit of the limitless possibilities of just being us. We have all heard others say what is not possible, what is hard, or what they or we cannot do, and we begin to limit our choices. Take some time to dream your big dream. If you have done this before, do it again and notice what has evolved and grown within you. If you could write a fairytale story about your life, what would it look like? Where would your life be? What would you do? Who would be there? How would you spend your time? How would it feel? The more you can connect with this as becoming a reality, the closer you are to walking the path towards your dreams coming true. This is sacred space for you to dream big. You might want to listen to this dream life meditation here—Episode 41 on the Body and Soul Wisdom Podcast or the Dream Life Meditation on Sound Cloud.
https://www.jenmons.com/podcast/podcast/envision-2020-your-dream-life-meditation

My Dream Life

Ideas/Notes

Ideas/Notes

Ideas/Notes

Ideas/Notes

Share the Love

Wow! You did it! You started the journey and committed to a daily practice of journaling and personal growth. Did you add this to your celebration list?! If you are on this page it means you have taken a step toward a daily devotion practice. It's okay if you missed a few days or even more here or there. That doesn't matter. You set the intention and committed to your personal reflection, growth, and self-awareness. You can continue this path with new journals in our upcoming series, join our Daily Devotion and 13 Moons memberships, explore growth our other programs, such as 5 Element Well-th and Prosperity, or continue journaling on your own and creating your own prompts. I hope you are happy with yourself. I am honored and grateful for your commitment to this experience. You deserve to be celebrated. __ here to join the presale and waitlist for the new journals.

I invite you to join our Facebook group and share your reflections, gratitudes, celebrations, and even your challenges. We have a group of light-minded souls ready to welcome you and walk beside you on this journey.

Facebook Groups
https://www.facebook.com/groups/13moonsdevotion
https://www.facebook.com/groups/5elementwellth

I created this journal with the feel and intuition of it being a sacred gift for a special someone. I often give them out at my workshops and retreats and mail them to private clients with their welcome gift box. If you loved this journal and the experience, I invite you to consider purchasing one as a gift for a friend or loved one for your next holiday, birthday, Mother's Day, or as a just because gift. Sharing the love allows you to be a part of the ripple effect for creating positive change in the world. **You were my intention when I created this.** I wanted to share this experience with as many people as possible to help facilitate positive habits in the lives of each and every person.

Take a moment to reflect upon the people in your life—your inner circle of influence and even throughout your community. Sharing this experience creates a positive current in the world and makes the world a better place. Who in your life would benefit from this experience? How will it help them? What might they learn? How might they grow?

As a thank you for sharing the love, I have created a 22% loving savings for your reorder.
Use Code

To purchase your journal Go to www.jenmons.com/dailydevotion

To join the membership go to: https://www.jenmons.com/13moons-of-devotion and use code dailydevotion22 for 22% Savings

Next Steps

True devotion means becoming the hand of the Divine. Whatever comes your way, you will know how to transform it into something beautiful.
— Sadhguru

A New Beginning....

Take a deep breath and take it all in. But don't stop now. Keep going! You have come so far. You have learned and grown in your own self-awareness and daily practice in more ways than you imagined when you set out to take part in this journey. My team and I are here to encourage and support you.

Have you ever been part of an amazing experience that ended and left you feeling, "Okay, what's next?" I have and I want to share options for continued growth on this path.

Join the complimentary Facebook community and do the daily prompts in community.
https://www.facebook.com/groups/13moonsdevotion

Join our annual membership where you will be invited to live monthly new moon ceremonies and seasonal planning workshops. Annual membership bonuses include access to a wellness resource library,

meditations, podcasts, and other resources as well as accountability and bonus calls with our team.
https://www.jenmons.com/13moons-of-devotion

Stay Connected, Join our Tribe. Receive weekly podcast episodes and invites to events.
https://www.jenmons.com/tribe

Purchase a new Journal Here
www.jenmons.com/dailydevotion

Online Courses
www.jenmonns/courses

Websites
www.jenmons.com
www.embodiedsoulcoachingacademy.com
www.5elementwellth.com
www.illuminateyoursoulretreats.com

Body and Soul Wisdom Podcast

Looking to dive deeper into a specific area?
I have taken the Top Elements of well-being and created five 75-day journals to serve as a catalyst in the different areas of well-being through 5 Element Well-th. They will be available in 2023. Visit www.jenmons.com/dailydevotion to get on the waitlist and be notified on the new journals below!

Mindset
Prosperity (Financial Freedom)

Spiritual (Embodied Soul Wisdom)
Body Well-being (Body Wisdom)
Emotional Empowerment & Freedom

The Creation of this Journal

I have always loved planning. I love organization and structure, but in the last 10 years I have learned to surrender into the flow of life. I always loved having a journal bedside which for many years was just a place for me to reflect on my daily life. As I began to create courses in my coaching career, I created eBooks and journals. My students and clients loved them. They loved having journal prompts, direction, and guidance. Guidance is a great way to jumpstart a healthy habit. It's like having a guided meditation vs. sitting in stillness with a clean slate. I have purchased journals and planners over the years for myself and received them as gifts but never found *the one* that blended all of the steps that I knew worked to bring a balance of intuition, intention, flow, strategy, structure, and cyclical planning. I wanted something that allowed me to blend the journaling with the planning. You can use this as a tool for personal or professional growth or the blend of both to create intention and clarity and direction in your life. The following is a list of resources that influenced the creation of this journal.

Do Less Planner by Kate Northrup
Faith Activated with Rachel Luna
Law of Attraction Daily Planner from Freedom Mastery
Morning Sidekick Journal by Habit Nest

I also compiled my life experiences and feedback from my membership and clients to create this journal.

There are many people who inspired the creation of this journal that I would like to highlight.

Disclaimer:

This content is being provided to you for your individual use. You are not permitted or authorized to copy, share, sell, post, distribute, reproduce, duplicate, trade, resell, exploit, or otherwise disseminate any portion of this content for business or commercial use, or in any other way that earns you money, without my prior written permission. This journal is for educational and personal development purposes only and not meant to replace support from any kind of healthcare professional or services. Please seek appropriate professional advice regarding physical or physiological conditions or concerns.

Resources

Moon Calendar: https://www.almanac.com/astronomy/moon/calendar

Moon Phases: https://www.space.com/18880-moon-phases.html

Gratitude:
https://www.psychologytoday.com/us/blog/mindful-anger/201807/science-proves-gratitude-is-key-well-being

Women's cycle
https://www.mindbodygreen.com/0-16167/get-to-know-the-4-phases-of-your-menstrual-cycle.html

COMMUNITY GIFTS:
Podcasts: Body and Soul Wisdom Podcast on Stitcher, Google, iTunes, and Spotify (Formerly The Embodied Healing Self since March 2019)

Meditation Bundle: https://jenmons.simplero.com/meditation-bundle

Facebook Group: https://www.facebook.com/groups/13moonsdevotion

Resources for New Moon and Cyclical Planning, Meditation Library, Self-Care and Wellness Tips, Bonus Templates for Seasonal Planning, Bonus Journals and Offerings available inside the 13 Moons of Daily Devotion Membership.

Sign up here https://www.jenmons.com/13moons-of-devotion

About the Author

Jen Mons, CHHC, ACC, RYT, LSH, ISOD -1, DH1

Jenny is a coach, mentor, and energy alchemist for purpose-driven women ready to live in 5 Element Well-th. Her work attracts healers, coaches, and conscious feminine leaders. She combines her training in holistic health coaching, life coaching, energy healing, meditation, yoga, spiritual healing, and reprogramming of the subconscious through divine healing to help high performing women redesign their energetic imprint to embody their soul wisdom and prosperity consciousness. Her clients see results including optimal well-being, financial freedom, healthy relationships, and energy management and create more peace, freedom, joy, and connection in their lives. She has facilitated workshops and retreats locally and internationally since 2014 and is the host of The Body and Soul Wisdom Podcast.

464

Her holistic approach is a blend of building a solid foundation through balanced well-being with compassionate emotional empowerment and intuitive spiritual guidance. She is the host of the Podcast "Body and Soul Wisdom," 5 Element Well-th and Prosperity, Illuminate Your Soul Retreats, and the North Star Collective for Healers, Coaches, and Conscious Feminine Leaders.

She coaches, mentors, and educates healers, coaches, and consciously driven entrepreneurs seeking natural balanced health, more energy, self-confidence, freedom, and fulfillment in their life by harnessing the energy of healing self-limiting beliefs and body and soul wisdom to step into our unique soul signature. Through her own life experiences and health crises, she has mastered creating the foundation for a blueprint that is an energetic vibrational match for the highest expression of our soul signature and is the creator of the 6 step process "Soul Wisdom Imprinting".

Jenny is a former Professional Mechanical Engineer, Federal Service Academy Graduate, USN reservist, and USCG licensed officer, whose own life threatening health challenges led her down a path towards holistic healing. She combines her training in holistic wellness, detoxification, spiritual healing, personal growth coaching, fitness, yoga, and meditation to serve her clients' needs. She uses the talents from her former career to create a structured system and results for clients through heart-centered support and intuitive guidance while inviting women to welcome a balance of feminine flow and strategy. In her free time, she enjoys yoga, dance, travel, and spending time on the ocean surfing, windsurfing, sailing, and boating with her husband and two daughters.

Social Media Links:

@jen.mons instagram

@JenMonsCoaching

Freebie download here:

Website https://www.jenmons.com/tribe

www.embodiedsoulcoachingacademy.com

Podcast The Body and Soul Wisdom Podcast (Formerly Embodied Healing Self)

What I love to speak/write about:

- 5 Element Well-th: The Path to Prosperity Consciousness
- Energy management and Biz Alchemy: The balance of Feminine flow and strategy
- The 6 Pillars of Soul Wisdom Imprinting. Clarity on owning your gifts
- Embodied Soul Wisdom
- Energy Mastery

For inquires please visit https://www.jenmons.com/contact

Made in the USA
Columbia, SC
28 November 2022

72015822R00259